Exercises in Historical Geology

Exercises In
Historical Geology

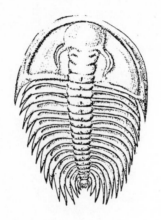

James W. Collinson

The Ohio State University

KENDALL/HUNT PUBLISHING COMPANY
DUBUQUE, IOWA

Printed in the United States of America

CONTENTS

Preface vii

1. Review of Earth Materials 1

2. The Principle of Uniformity 8

3. Facies Relationships 14

4. Relative Dating—Sequences of Events 39

5. Geochronometry 45

6. Ohio Fossils 49

7. Trilobite Biostratigraphy 50

8. Paleomagnetism and Sea-floor Spreading 56

9. Ocean Floors 65

10. Interpretation of Geologic Maps 71

11. Geologic Map of Ohio 78

12. Regional Geology of the United States 81

13. Canadian Shield—Core of the Continent 89

14. Interior Lowland—The Stable Interior 93

15. Folded Appalachian Mountains 94

16. Colorado Plateau and Ancient Colorado Mountains 99

17. Black Hills and the High Plains 103

18. Pleistocene Glaciation 107

19. Lunar Geology 111

These laboratory exercises are specifically designed to supplement lectures in the introductory level historical geology course at Ohio State University. Exercises 1-4, 10, and 13-19 are from *Interpreting Earth History* by M.S. Peterson and J.K. Rigby. Exercises 5-9, 11, and 12 evolved over several academic quarters with the aid and suggestions of graduate students in charge of laboratory sessions. The latter exercises are less self-contained than the former, and they require more explanation and demonstration by the laboratory instructor. Many more exercises are included than can be covered in the average course; each lecturer may select those exercises that are most relevant to his course. Parts of some exercises, such as 1, 4, and 10, are useful as homework assignments in preparation for other exercises.

J.W.C.

Review of
Earth Materials

The fundamental building blocks of earth materials are atoms. Specific combinations of atoms build solid, crystalline, inorganic substances known as minerals. **Minerals** are defined as natural inorganic substances of reasonably definite chemical composition, with an orderly internal atomic arrangement, which produces certain specific physical characteristics (*e.g.*, color, hardness, density, etc.).

Rocks are combinations of minerals which are consolidated by any one of several natural earth processes. Based on their origin, rocks are classified into three groups: (1) Igneous; (2) Sedimentary; and (3) Metamorphic. The rock cycle, diagrammed in Figure 1-1, illustrates the relationships between the three groups of rocks and the earth processes involved in their formation.

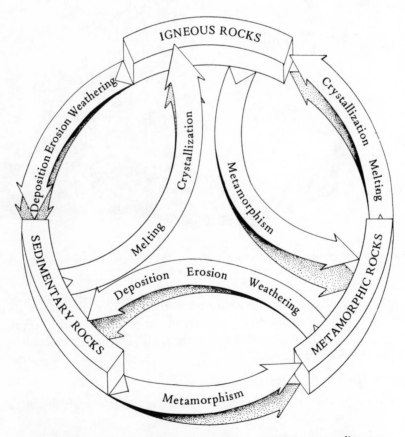

Figure 1-1. The rock cycle. The three main groups of rocks, igneous, sedimentary, and metamorphic, are produced by the operation of earth processes. Each of the three may be derived from the other two by these processes. The inclined arrows illustrate the passage of time as the cycle continues.

1

Igneous Rocks

Igneous rocks are those rocks that have formed by crystallization of melted rock material during cooling. Igneous rocks are formed either on or beneath the earth's surface. Molten material beneath the surface is called magma, and its crystallization produces intrusive igneous rocks. When magma reaches the surface of the earth it is called lava and when cooled crystallizes into extrusive igneous rocks. Igneous rocks are classified into groups based upon their texture (size, shape, and boundary relations of individual grains), and their mineral composition.

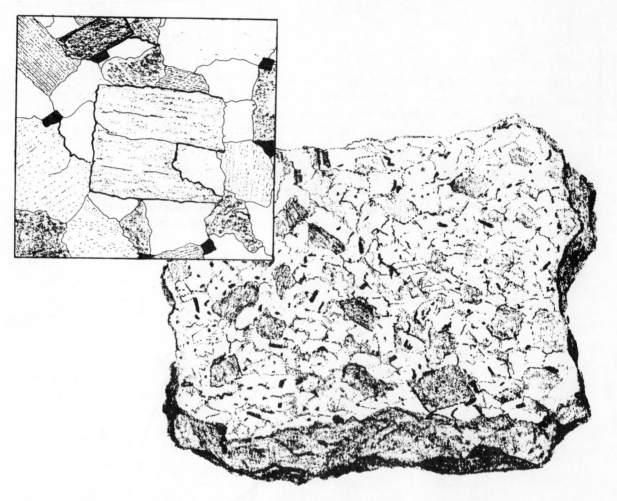

Figure 1-2. A hand specimen of granite, an intrusive igneous rock. The enlargement is a view through a microscope and illustrates the interlocking crystalline texture characteristic of igneous rocks.

The texture of igneous rocks, both intrusive and extrusive, is a mosaic of interlocking crystals (Figure 1-2). Intrusive igneous rocks are characterized by large, easily visible crystals produced by a slow cooling rate. Crystals of extrusive igneous rocks are small, essentially microscopic in size, and are small because the lava cooled quickly.

The common types of igneous textures are as follows:

COARSE-GRAINED: large crystals which are easily distinguishable with the unaided eye, typical of intrusive rocks.

PORPHYRITIC: coarse-grained with two sizes of crystals, one much larger than the other. The larger crystals are called phenocrysts.

FINE-GRAINED: microscopic mineral grains, typical of extrusive rocks.

Texture		Color (Mineral Composition)		
		Light	Medium	Dark
Intrusive	Coarse-Grained	Granite	Diorite	Gabbro
Extrusive	Fine-Grained	Rhyolite	Andesite	Basalt
Extrusive	Vesicular	Pumice		Scoria
Extrusive	Glassy	Obsidian		
Extrusive	Fragmental	Tuff & Breccia		

Figure 1-3. A classification of igneous rocks.

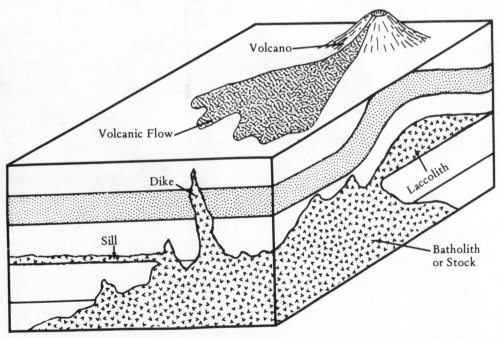

Figure 1-4. A cross-section of part of the earth's crust showing the typical shape and relationships of the most common types of igneous bodies.

VESICULAR: fine-grained mass with numerous air-holes formed by trapped gas within the lava, found exclusively in extrusive rocks.

GLASSY: a non-crystalline solid, having the appearance of glass, found in extrusive rocks which have cooled very rapidly.

FRAGMENTAL: composed of rock fragments of variable size and shape called tefra, found exclusively in extrusive rocks.

Sedimentary Rocks

Sedimentary rocks are those which are formed from accumulated fragments of previously formed rocks and minerals which are subsequently consolidated by cementation and compaction. Sedimentary rocks are the most abundant type of rock on the earth's surface. They are characterized by layered construction which is caused by variation in the constituent minerals or grains as they accumulated. Fossils, the remains of previously living organisms, are found essentially only in sedimentary rocks.

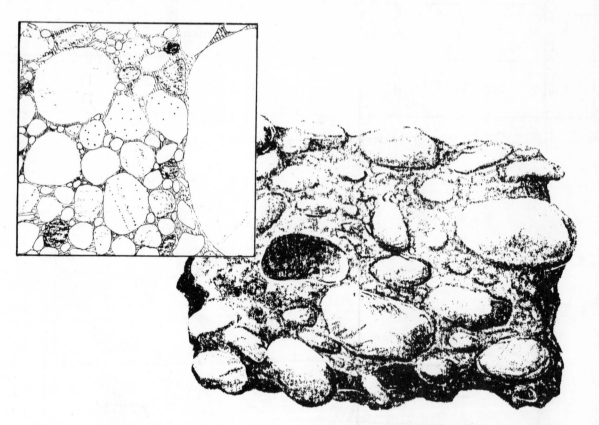

Figure 1-5. A hand specimen of conglomerate, a coarse-grained sedimentary rock. The enlargement is a view showing the discrete transported particles cemented together in a texture typical of sedimentary rocks.

Sedimentary rocks are classified on the basis of their grain-size and texture and their composition (Figure 1-6).

4

Sediments	Sedimentary Rocks	Symbols	Characteristics
Calcareous Particles $CaCO_3$	Limestone		Calcareous grains and skeletal fragments cemented with calcite, often containing fossils. Effervesces in dilute HCl.
Dolomite $CaMg(CO_3)_2$	Dolomite		Dolomite grains commonly resulting from alteration of limestone. Effervesces only in powdered form.
Sand	Sandstone		Sand-sized grains, (1/16 mm–2 mm) mainly of quartz, cemented by silica, calcite, or clay.
Gravel	Conglomerate		Rounded coarse-grained (> 2 mm) rock particles usually cemented by silica or calcite.
Clay and Silt	Shale or Mudstone		Clay and quartz grains of silt-size (< 1/16 mm) or smaller forming a platy structure.
Plant remains	Coal		Lignite, bituminous, or anthracite, formed by the alteration of plant debris.
Gypsum $CaSO_4 \cdot 2H_2O$	Gypsum		Occurs normally in sedimentary rocks as thin interbedded layers, formed by the evaporation of mineral-rich waters.
Halite $NaCl$	Rock Salt		Accumulated by the evaporation of sea water.

Figure 1-6. Classification of sedimentary rocks and their sediment sources. Symbols are shown as used in standard publications and throughout the manual.

Metamorphic Rocks

Metamorphic rocks are those igneous and sedimentary rocks which have been altered by high temperatures, high pressures, or both. Metamorphism changes the mineralogic and textural character of the original rock, producing rocks which are unique to this process (Figure 1-8). Some metamorphic rocks (gneiss and schist) display thin banding or layering in hand specimens. A metamorphic environment may be produced by deep burial, folding of the rocks, or igneous intrusion.

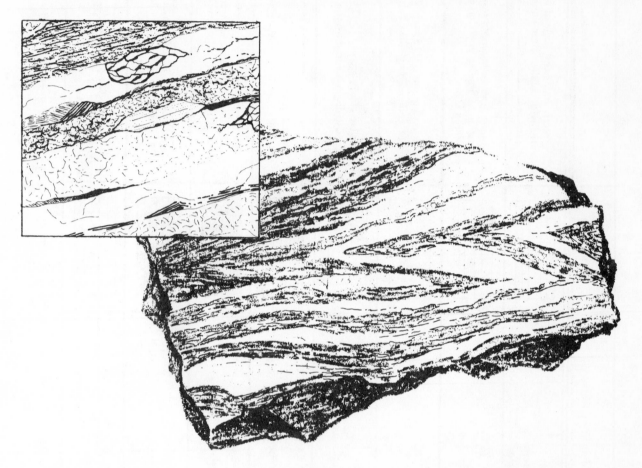

Figure 1-7. A hand specimen of gneiss, a banded metamorphic rock. The enlarged view shows the typical texture. The banded or lineated texture is typical of metamorphic rocks.

Procedure

1. Identify each of the supplied rock specimens in the study set.
2. Summarize the origin and history of each specimen.

Parent Rock	Metamorphic Rock	Characteristics
Limestone or Dolomite	Marble	Coarsely crystalline, commonly white, though variable in color, effervesces in dilute HCl.
Shale	Slate	Resembles shale, except much harder, cleavage plates form at angles to bedding of parent rock.
Sandstone	Quartzite	Massive, hard, interlocking grains of quartz bound so tightly that fracturing will break through the individual grains of quartz.
Shale, Basalt, Gabbro, or Tuff	Schist	Mineral grains are elongated producing a laminated appearance called foliation.
Conglomerate	Metaconglomerate	Resembles conglomerate, except much harder, fractures break through the pebbles.
Impure Sedimentary Rocks and Granite	Gneiss	Mineral grains form sub-parallel light and dark bands.

Figure 1-8. Metamorphic rocks, their characteristics, and parent materials.

7

EXERCISE 2

The Principle of Uniformity

The Principle of Uniformity, proposed by James Hutton, a Scotsman, in 1785 is the fundamental philosophical tenet by which the present understanding of the history of the earth has been derived. A definition of the principle is: past earth events can be described by present earth processes, or the present is the key to the past. For example, the excavation of the Grand Canyon is accounted for by the erosive force of the Colorado River rather than by a cataclysmic event such as a fracture opening up the earth's crust.

The principle implies a uniformity to the laws of nature, a view shared by all scientific disciplines. The rates, however, by which processes were operative certainly varied through time, particularly in Precambrian history where the earth's environment was likely quite different from today, therefore, literal interpretation of uniformity is misleading. Geologists generally agree that at least during post-Precambrian earth history, processes and rates have been sufficiently uniform to make the principle a workable tenet.

Uniformitarianism can be applied, as an example, by examination of modern depositional environments and comparison with ancient sedimentary deposits. The environment under which sediments are deposited is highly varied with respect to physical and chemical conditions. Because of this variation, sedimentary rocks differ and reflect the unique conditions under which they were deposited.

The outline below describes various sedimentary environments and the resulting characteristics of each:

I. MARINE (deposited in oceans or marginal seas)

  A. HIGH ENERGY (within wave-base) OR ROUGH, SHALLOW-WATER ENVIRONMENT CHARACTERISTICS:

    1. Deposition of medium to coarse sedimentary particles.

    2. Constant agitation and reworking of sedimentary material.

    3. Disarray and fracture of organic skeletal structures (shells).

    Resulting Sedimentary Rocks:

      a. Sandstone and conglomerate rock bodies.

      b. Moderately well-developed stratification in rocks.

      c. Fossils characteristically broken and skeletal structures disoriented.

  B. LOW ENERGY (below wave-base) OR QUIET, DEEP-WATER ENVIRONMENT CHARACTERISTICS:

    1. Quiet accumulation of fine sediments, rarely disturbed by water motions.

    2. Abundant benthonic organisms, both epifauna (surface) and infauna (subsurface) dwellers.

8

Resulting Sedimentary Rocks:

    a. Shale and siltstone rock bodies.

    b. Well-developed stratification, sometimes graded from coarse to fine upward in a sequence.

    c. Fossils generally unbroken and unsorted, and often composed of planktonic organisms.

C. ORGANIC REEF ENVIRONMENT CHARACTERISTICS

    1. Vertical development of unbedded skeletal material, both living and dead, whose upper surface is above the wave-base (reef proper).

    2. Seaward accumulation of eroded fragments of reef (fore-reef).

    3. Lagoon where fine calcareous sand may accumulate in flat-lying deposits, abundant organisms present (back-reef).

Resulting Sedimentary Rocks:

    a. Massive, non-bedded calcareous mound or lens-shaped deposit consisting of inter-grown fossils, including algae, sponges, corals, and other types.

    b. Fore-reef deposits of limestone, composed of reef-fragments in steeply inclined bedded strata.

    c. Back-reef lagoonal deposits of flat-lying and thin bedded, highly fossiliferous limestone, but may grade to unfossiliferous dolomite or evaporites.

II. NON MARINE (deposits on land)

  A. FLUVIAL (Stream deposited material) ENVIRONMENT CHARACTERISTICS:

    1. Transportation and deposition of poorly to moderately sorted, well-rounded rock particles, ranging in size from silt to boulders.

    2. Deposition in irregular, elongate and lenticular stream channels or valleys.

    3. Terrestrial plants and animals living near streams.

Resulting Sedimentary Rocks:

    a. Deposits of conglomerate and sandstone rock bodies composed of well-rounded, poorly to moderately sorted rock particles.

    b. Poorly stratified deposit with lenticular beds and nearly planar, shallow cross-bedding.

    c. Fossils rare, consisting of land animals and plant remains.

  B. LACUSTRINE (deposited in lakes) ENVIRONMENT CHARACTERISTICS:

    1. Quiet, slow accumulation of sediments with excellent sorting of particle sizes in interior; margin of lacustrine basin may have coarser beach zone.

    2. Fresh-water animals and plants exclusively.

Resulting Sedimentary Rocks:

    a. Uniformly textured siltstone and shale rock bodies often showing highly regular continuous, alternating light and dark layers called varves, resulting from seasonal variation of depositional environment. Basin margin deposits may be coarse beach-like accumulations.

    b. Presence of fossils of fresh-water organisms, plant and animal.

  C. PALUDAL (swamp and marsh deposits) ENVIRONMENT CHARACTERISTICS:

    1. Slow, discontinuous accumulation of fine sedimentary material.

    2. Abundant plant life living and accumulating in the area.

Resulting Sedimentary Rocks:

    a. Organic-rich shale and sandstone or coal deposits with thin stringers of siltstone and shale (boney coal).

    b. Plant fossils common in all stages of preservation.

D. AEOLIAN (wind-blown deposits) ENVIRONMENT CHARACTERISTICS:

    1. Slow accumulation of extremely well-sorted fine-grained, often rounded sedimentary particles.

    2. Deposition of material as dunes with concave bedding on leeward side, changing direction of deposition with variation in wind direction.

Resulting Sedimentary Rocks:

    a. Sandstone rocks composed of rounded and very well-sorted particles of quartz or other resistant minerals. The surface of each well-rounded particle is often pitted or frosted.

    b. Well-developed, moderately high concave cross-beds up to tens-of-feet in length.

E. GLACIAL ENVIRONMENT CHARACTERISTICS:

    1. Massive erosion and transportation of large amounts of unsorted angular sediments, particles ranging from clay to boulder or large block size within and along the margins of a glacier.

    2. Reworking of sedimentary particles by action of meltwater with deposition as stratified deposits in front of melting glacier.

Resulting Sedimentary Rocks:

    a. Unsorted individual angular particles which may be striated on their surface due to the grinding action of rocks against each other, deposited in clayey matrix.

    b. Mound or ridge-like deposits of unsorted particles of all sizes called moraines.

    c. Stratified deposits of fine silt and sand-sized material, sometimes reworked by wind and deposited as loess.

Procedure

On the following three pages are photographs of modern environments, shown in the left column and sedimentary rock types on the right (Figures 2-1, 2-2 and 2-3).

1. Using the Principle of Uniformity as a guide, match the sedimentary rock with the appropriate modern environment as described in the outline above.

2. Which sedimentary rocks of those illustrated are the most difficult to match? Which are the most obvious? Why?

Low Energy Marine Environment, Grand Cayman Island, B.W.I.

A. _____

Paludal Environment, Southern Louisiana.

B. _____

Organic Reef Environment, East end Grand Cayman Island, B.W.I.

C. _____

Figure 2-1.

High Energy Marine Environment, North Carolina Coast
(photo by H.J. Bissell).

D. _____

Coal

Aeolian Environment, Peruvian sand dunes (photo by D.L. Boyd).

E. _____

Glacial Environment, Iceland (photo by Robert Dickman).

F. _____

Figure 2-2.

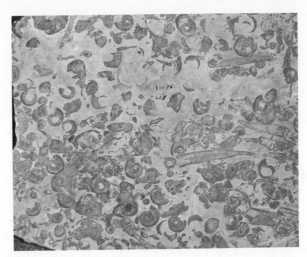

Fluvial Environment, Provo River, Utah.

G. _____

Figure 2-3.

EXERCISE 3

===

Facies Relationships

The term **facies**, as used outside geologic terminology, means merely aspect or general appearance, however, in the geologic literature, the term facies is used to denote essentially contemporaneous rocks of differing lithologies due to differing environments. It is also used as a description of one type of rock through a major portion of geologic time. For example, the term red-bed facies has been utilized to contrast with the gray sediments of adjacent areas, or the term black-shale facies has been utilized to contrast with the more nearly normal marine-appearing rocks. Facies in sedimentary rocks are the result of variations in sedimentary environments during deposition. If one were to look at the seafloor off any of the present coastlines, one would see considerable variation in the kinds of sediments being deposited, coarse gravel or sand along the beach zone, grading offshore into silt or mud. In some areas, organisms produce carbonate masses, or reef-like structures. If these same sedimentary belts continue through time a series of blocks of similarly textured sediments would be deposited which might be classed as sedimentary facies, or as **lithofacies**, in contrast with the depositional pattern associated with particular biologic groups which are termed **biofacies**.

Biofacies and lithofacies are the result of sediments and organisms to a variety of factors in the environment, such as texture of substrate, chemistry in terms of the amount of oxygen and carbon dioxide available, salinity, water turbulence, and turbidity. These as well as other factors influence the characteristics of the sedimentary and biologic association which we see in the geologic record as facies of either sedimentary rocks or biologic associations.

Early geologists who studied the bedrock of Europe and North America thought primarily in terms of uniform layers of rocks which extended virtually worldwide and which were deposited from a primeval sea. They had complex interpretations to explain away areas where such presumably world-wide uniform patterns were not consistent. Near the turn of the century, lateral variations in contemporaneous series were recognized, and a new study of facies relationships began.

If all aspects of an environment remained constant during some period in geologic time, a series of vertical belts would develop, such as that illustrated in Figure 3-1. Depth of water; composition, and texture of sediments being introduced; rate of sedimentation; rate of subsidence and other factors have remained constant, building a series of sedimentary rocks with relatively constant patterns. Such constancy in the geologic record is rare, however, and generally the environment varies, resulting in a lateral shift in the kinds of rocks which are produced such as illustrated in Figure 3-2. In this relationship the facies belts, or the areas of sedimentation of various textures of sedimentary rocks, have migrated toward the left, as a result of increase in coarseness and of the amount of material being transported into the sedimentary basin. The rate of sedimentation was more rapid than the rate of subsidence, resulting in filling of the sedimentary basin on one side and ultimately crowding the shoreline to the left, expanding the land mass at the expense of the area covered by the sea. The thickness of sediment deposited during any one time interval in Figures 3-1 and 3-2 remained relatively constant. There was no development of a thick wedge of clastic sediments towards the source area. If the rate of sedimentation were influenced by rapid subsidence in the area of coarse

14

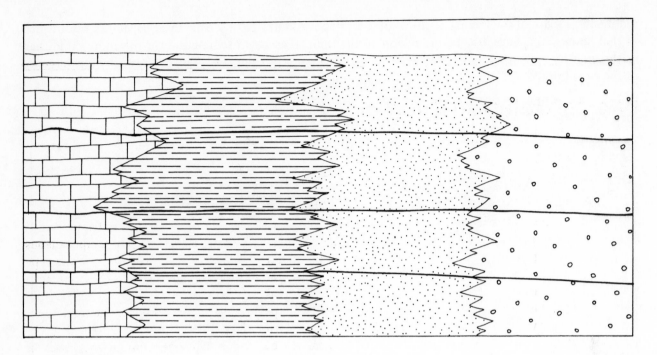

Figure 3-1. Schematic cross-section showing facies relationships under static conditions of subsidence and sediment supply. The dark horizontal lines delineate synchronous units.

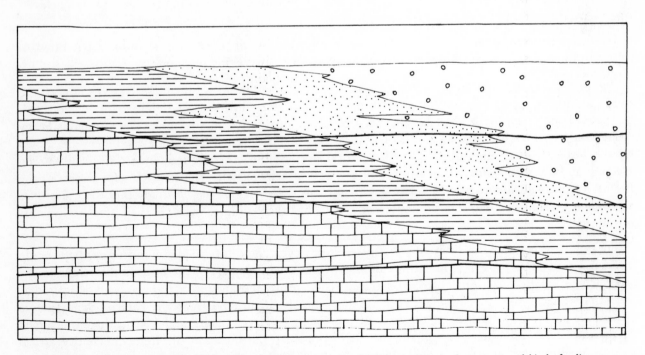

Figure 3-2. Schematic cross-section showing facies variations produced by fluctuations in the amount and kind of sediments deposited under uniform conditions of subsidence.

sediments, a marked thickening of the sediments deposited during any time interval should result, such as that shown in Figure 3-3. In the region to the right, the rate of sedimentation was more rapid than in the area to the left and a thicker sequence of sediments accumulated. This is shown by a divergence of the time lines.

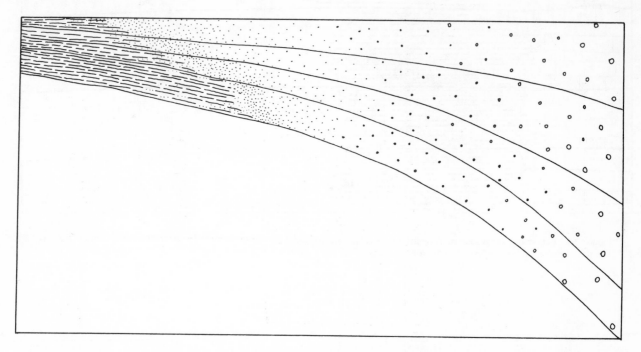

Figure 3-3. Schematic cross-section showing facies relationships under conditions of varying subsidence and sediment supply. The curved lines represent time lines whose positions were determined by fossils.

In facies studies, therefore, one can obtain some inference in terms of relative rates of sedimentation, direction of transport, and capacity of the transporting medium.

Figure 3-4 is a restored cross-section of Cambrian rocks visible in walls of the Grand Canyon, and shows an intertonguing relationship of dolomite and limestone in the west (left) with an eastern belt of shale. Time lines, established by the occurrence of distinctive fossil faunas, are shown as heavy dashed, approximately horizontal lines. The locations of measured stratigraphic sequences are shown by the heavy dashed vertical lines. In the central part of the cross-section, limestones can be seen grading laterally into thin tongues of dolomite which interfinger with shales in the upper part of the Bright Angel Shale. Intertonguing relationships such as these suggest very strongly that the limestones are time-equivalents of the thin dolomite beds, and that the dolomite beds are the lateral equivalents of the shale.

To the east, beyond the limit of the cross-section, even these intermediate and upper beds grade into sandstone. The pattern is much like that shown in the lower part of the measured sections to the west, where Bright Angel Shale is demonstrated to be contemporaneous or to have been deposited at the same time as the beds of the Tapeats Sandstone. In Figure 3-4 the term Tapeats Sandstone is applied to all of the sandstone at the base of the Cambrian section, although beds in the eastern part of the exposure are much younger than those in the west. On the basis of lateral continuity, stratigraphic position, and lithology, the Tapeats Sandstone beds in the west are correlated to the east as

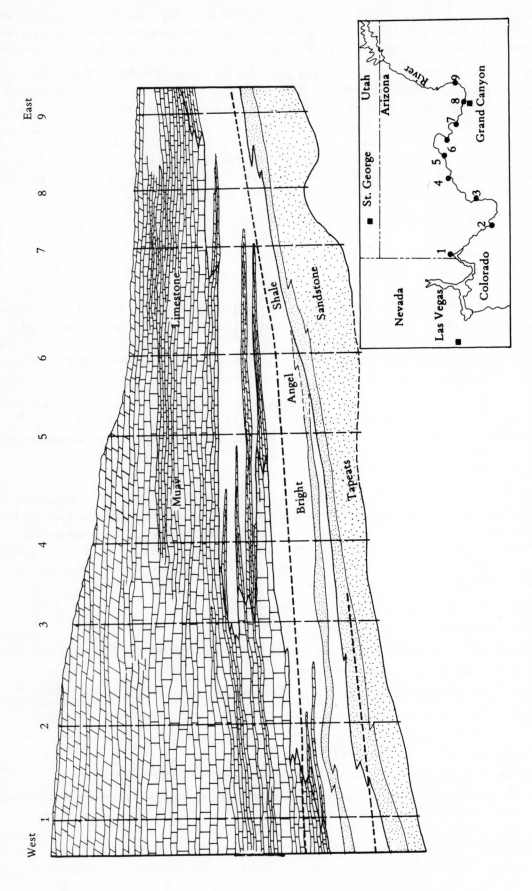

Figure 3-4. Restored cross-section of Cambrian rocks in the Grand Canyon area of northern Arizona, from Lake Mead east to the junction of the Little Colorado and Colorado Rivers (courtesy Carnegie Institute of Washington, publication 563, October 1945 by E. McKee, the following material: modified diagram after fig. 1, p. 14).

part of a continuous sandstone body, even though of slightly differing ages. One can speak of the sandstone facies at the base of the Cambrian rocks in contrast to the shale facies which overlies it, and in turn to the dolomite and limestone facies which is represented in the younger rocks.

To some extent the Cambrian rocks demonstrate what has been termed **Walther's Law or Principle** which is that in vertical sequence the superjacent facies grade laterally into one another. For example, the Bright Angel Shale overlies the Tapeats Sandstone, and grades laterally into it. Similarly in the central part of the section, dolomite and shale units are interbedded and grade laterally into one another. Although not infallible, the general observation holds, that various kinds of rocks which are superjacent to one another in a stratigraphic sequence also grade laterally into one another along the outcrop band unless some external event interrupts. This relationship can be seen in shale, sandstone and conglomerate sequences, as well as in limestone, dolomite and evaporite sequences.

Procedure
Part I

The first part of the exercise utilizes the Devonian rocks in New York and Pennsylvania. Fifteen somewhat generalized stratigraphic sections, which were measured through the Devonian rocks at localities approximately 20 miles apart, are plotted as logs in Figure 3-5. Section 1 is toward the west and Section 15 is toward the east, in a traverse which lies generally along the New York-Pennsylvania border. Symbols of the lithology are those used in previous exercises.

Total thickness of the preserved sections are shown to scale. Various time lines have been established by the use of fossils and are shown by a series of dots through each column and are marked by small letters. The various time horizons or levels of contemporaneous deposition are shown by the same letters. For example, all the rocks immediately below the dotted line marked "a" in each of the 15 sections were deposited contemporaneously.

1. Construct a restored section for these Devonian rocks similar to the example of Cambrian rocks in Figure 3-3. Tear out the pages containing Figures 3-5 (A-E) and connect the various sections together in sequence from 1 to 15. Maintain the datum elevation of 2500 feet as a horizontal line, to keep the relative positions of all sections constant. With symbols interconnect various lithologic units and show the facies relationships of the relatively coarse-grained rocks in the east to the fine-grained rocks in the west.

2. Does Walther's Law apply to these rocks? Are there exceptions?

3. Are all of the conglomerates of the same age?

4. What trend is visible in the sandstone beds as they are traced from east to west?

5. Why do shale beds thin as traced from west to east?

6. What happens to the sandstone which occurs near the base of sections of 2, 3, 14, 15?

7. What is suggested by the small lens of conglomerate near the top of section 3 in the time interval between "f" and "g"?

8. From which direction were the sediments transported?

9. By what media (wind, glaciers, streams, marine currents) were the sediments transported?

10. When was the period of maximum velocity of transporting currents? Where is the area of most rapid subsidence? When did it occur?

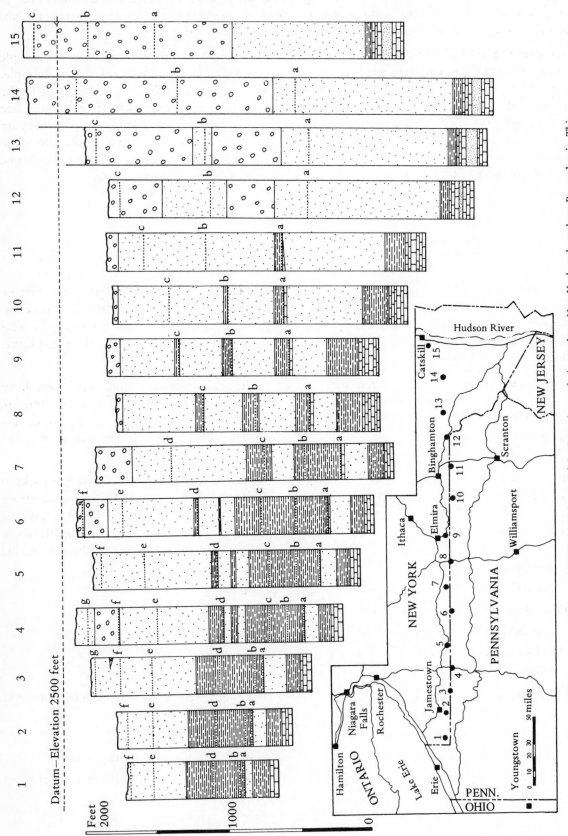

Figure 3-5. A series of fifteen stratigraphic columns of the Devonian rocks in southern New York and northern Pennsylvania. This sequence is a classic example of intergrading facies (adapted from Broughton, *et al.*, 1962).

19

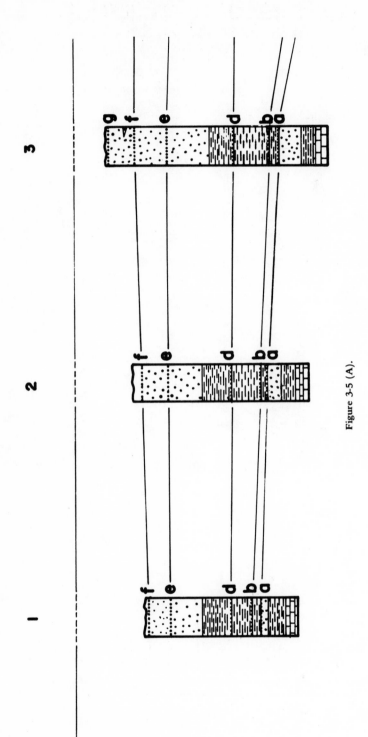

Figure 3-5 (A).

21

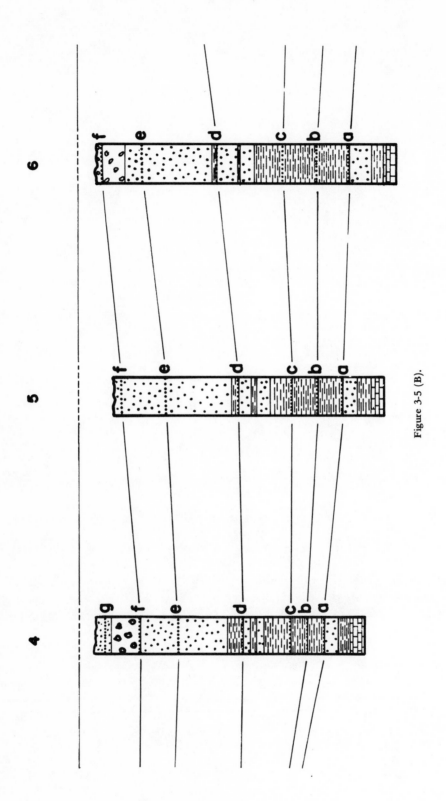

Figure 3-5 (B).

23

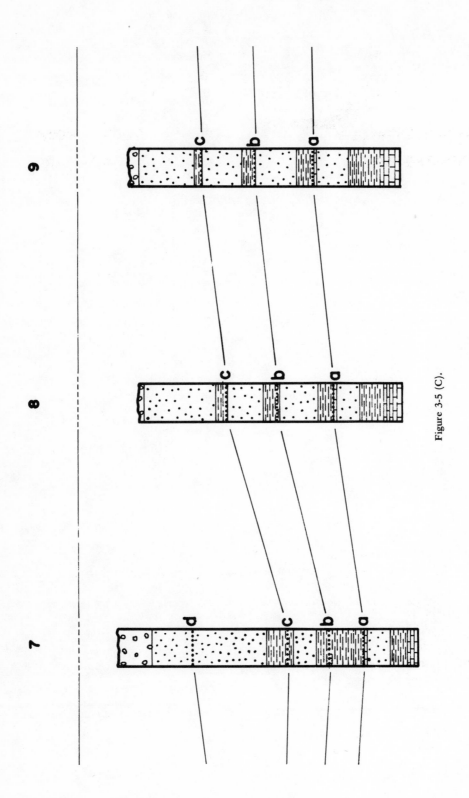

Figure 3-5 (C).

25

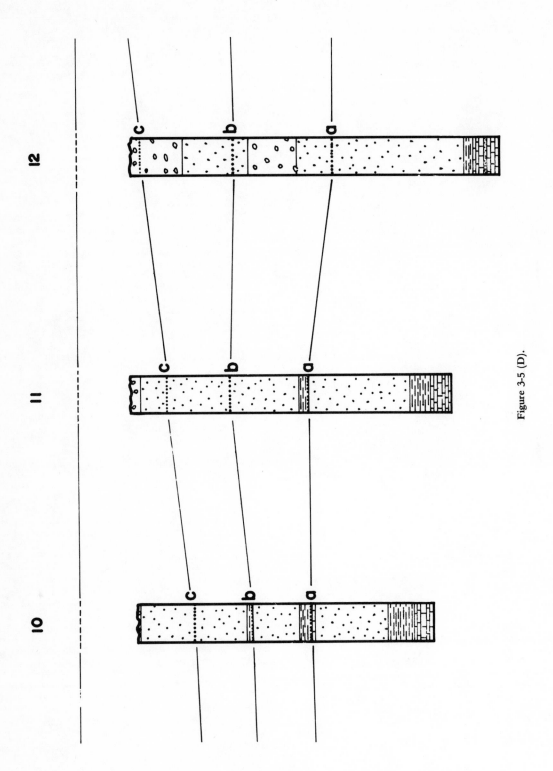

Figure 3-5 (D).

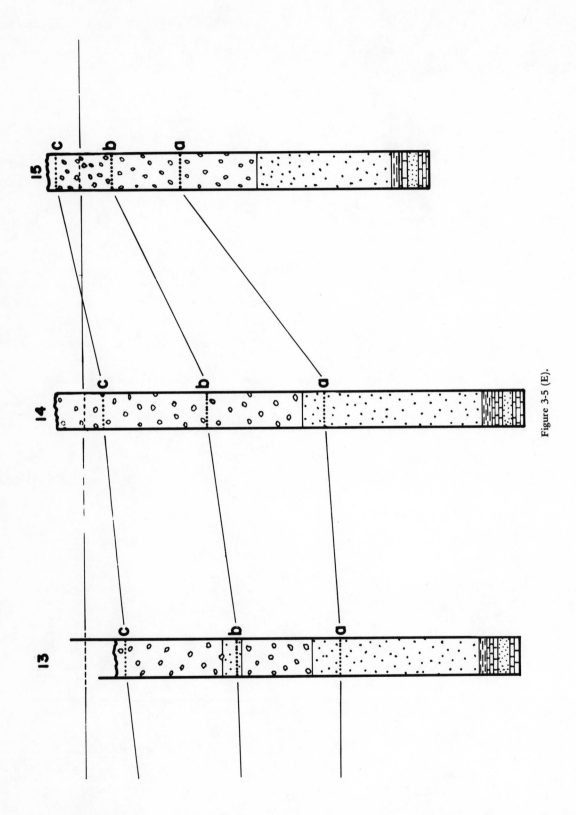

Figure 3-5 (E).

29

Part II

Ten stratigraphic columns shown in Figure 3-6 document the facies relationships through the classic Capitan Reef in the Guadalupe Mountains of Texas and New Mexico, one of the major carbonate reef-masses in North America. This series of stratigraphic sections is oriented approximately northwest to southeast. Bedded limestone is shown with the normal brick-like symbol but massive limestone is shown with an open discontinuous pattern. Gypsum, or evaporites, are shown with a close-spaced diagonal grid in sections at both the eastern and western margins.

1. Construct a restored cross section. Tear out the page of stratigraphic sections and cut them apart. Separate them about 3 inches to more closely approximate the relationships on a more natural scale and glue them to a large sheet using the top of the Brushy Canyon Formation as a horizontal datum. The dotted lines which cross-connect between the various stratigraphic sections are time lines and are labeled with letters like those in the Devonian diagram of Part I.

2. Are the massive reef limestones of Section 3 the same age as the massive reef limestones of Section 7? Are those of 3 contemporaneous to those of the upper part of Section 6?

3. What is the age of the massive dolomite in Section 2 in relationship to limestone beds of the Cherry Canyon Formation?

4. What is the age of the thin gypsum bed at the top of Section 1 in relationship to the rocks in Sections 8 and 9?

5. What is the direction of growth through time of the reef mass?

6. It is generally felt that the Cherry Canyon Formation contact with the top of the Brushy Canyon Formation remained essentially horizontal during deposition of these Permian reefs and that the top of the reef or the top of the massive dolomite was near sea level. In what depth of water was the gypsum in the top of Section 1 deposited? What was the water depth during the deposition of the gypsum in Section 9 and 10?

7. From the diagram, which sequence would be termed back-reef and which sequence would be termed basin or fore-reef facies?

Part III

The stratigraphic profile shown in Figure 3-7 is an east-west series of stratigraphic sections through the Upper Cretaceous rocks of central and eastern Utah. The profile shows relationships of the clastic wedge associated with a pulse of the Laramide Orogeny in western North America.

1. Construct a restored cross-section of these Cretaceous rocks using the same techniques as applied to the Devonian and Permian rocks in Parts 1 and 2.

2. What is the direction of transport of the sediments?

3. What is the relative rate of subsidence compared to the rate of sedimentation? What is your evidence?

4. What is the environment of coal deposits?

5. Is the pattern transgressive or regressive?

6. When was the most evident pulse of uplift in the source area during this part of the Laramide Orogeny? What are the evidences?

Part IV

If one can document the kind of sediments deposited at any one moment in time over a wide area, one can construct lithofacies maps to show patterns of sedimentation. Data summarized in Figure 3-8

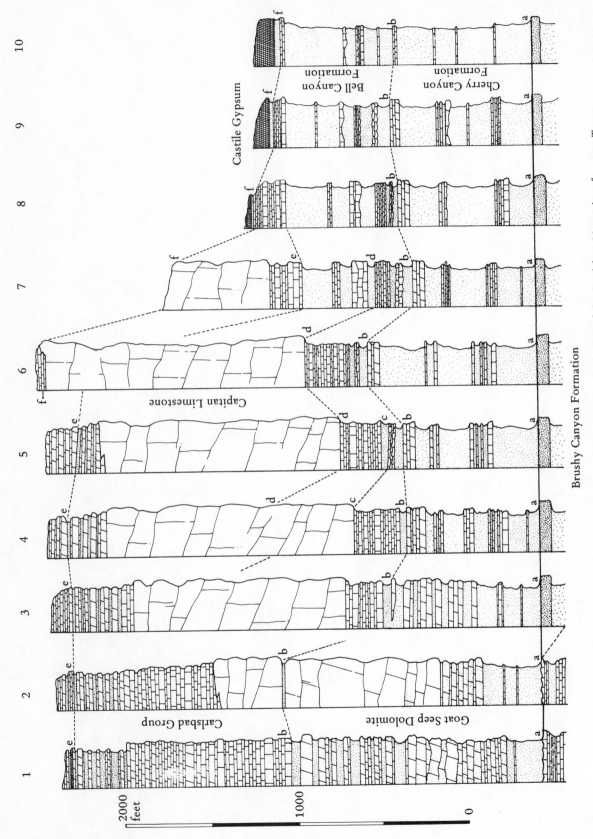

Figure 3-6. A series of 10 stratigraphic columns through the famed reef complex of the Guadalupe Mountains of western Texas and southern New Mexico (adapted from P.B. King, 1948).

Castile Gypsum

Bell Canyon Formation

Cherry Canyon Formation

Capitan Limestone

Goat Seep Dolomite

Carlsbad Group

Brushy Canyon Formation

2000 feet

1000

0

33

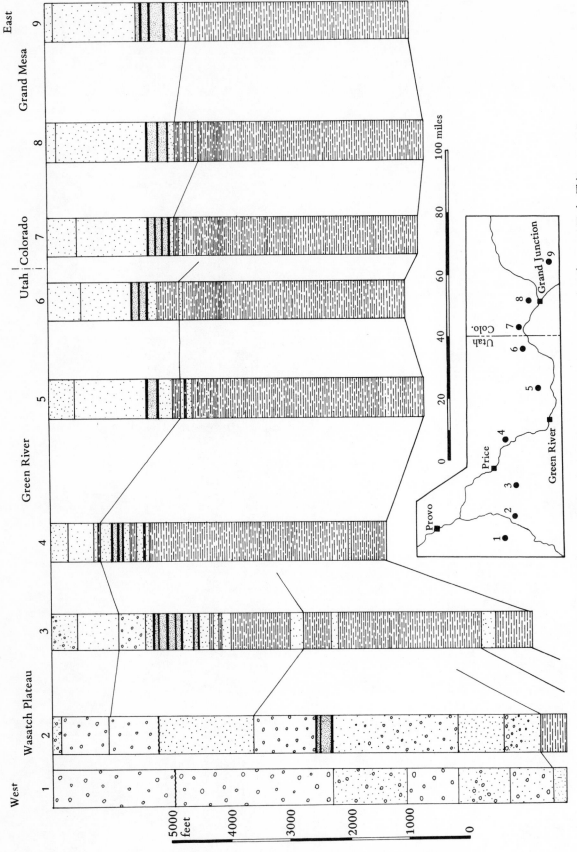

Figure 3-7. A series of nine stratigraphic sections through the Upper Cretaceous rocks of eastern Utah. This represents a cross-section through a coal-bearing clastic wedge (adapted from E.M. Speiker, 1949).

35

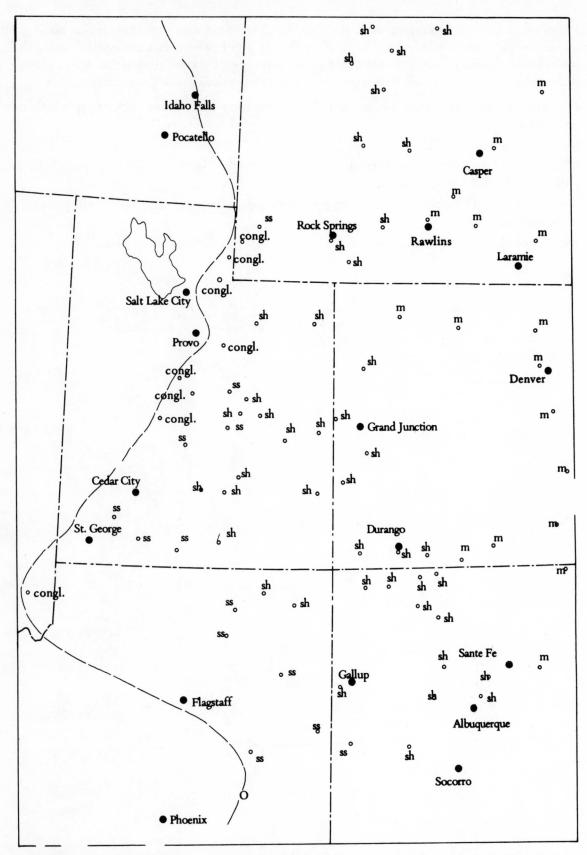

Figure 3-8. A map showing distribution of rock types of part of the Upper Cretaceous clastic wedge in the Mountain West. This is an area between the stable area of the continent and the western mobile belt.

on a map of part of the Mountain West, is of the kinds of rocks resulting from sediments deposited during the Middle-Upper Cretaceous. The small circles are points where data are available and lithology at each is shown by the following series of abbreviations: congl. for conglomerate, ss. for sandstone, sh. for shale and m for marl or chalk. The line of zero thickness is shown along the west.

1. Construct a lithofacies map by drawing lines separating the various rock types which can be recognized.

2. Do the facies belts parallel the zero thickness line?

3. What is the direction of transport of the sediments? What is the probable origin of the coarse sediments along the western border?

4. Were the Colorado Rocky Mountains present during deposition of these sedimentary rocks? What is the evidence?

5. Where would you expect the greatest thickness of sediments to have accumulated? Why?

Relative Dating, Sequences of Events

The study of the immensity of time is one of the unique features of the Science of Geology. In this exercise, however, we will be concerned only with the relative sequence of events; that is, event A preceded event B, or geologic feature A is older than geologic feature B, but younger than geologic feature C. Such geologic dating is referred to as relative dating where one event is established as older or younger in relationship to another.

Relative geologic ages are established primarily with three fundamental concepts. First, sedimentary rocks, in the main, were deposited originally horizontally. Any marked variation from horizontal attitude or bedding indicates some movement of the earth's crust. The original horizontal attitude of most sedimentary units has been described in what is formally called the **Principle of Original Horizontality.**

Second, those rocks which are highest in a normal undisturbed stratigraphic sequence are youngest, or conversely, those which are lowest in the undisturbed sequence were deposited first and are oldest. The second major principle in terms of relative dating has been formulated as the **Principle of Superposition.** In many canyon walls, for example in the Grand Canyon, rocks along the canyon rim were deposited over rock layers or formations exposed lower on the canyon walls. Thus, those beds along the canyon rim are younger than those exposed in the inner gorge and in the lower part of the Grand Canyon.

Third, geologic structures or rock bodies which cross-cut other rock bodies or structures are younger than the features which are cut. The third major principle of relative dating is commonly called the **Principle of Cross-cutting Relationships.** Geologically speaking, faults or dikes which cross-cut or which break series of strata are younger than deposition of the strata. In some instances additional horizontal sedimentary beds have been deposited over old fault surfaces, burying them, and providing evidence of the time of origin of the faults.

An example of a fault is shown in Figure 4-1A. The black bed, layer 2, in both blocks A and B was deposited as part of the same originally horizontal sheet. As a result of faulting, one block has moved down relative to the other, at some time after deposition of the black horizontal bed and the overlying bed 3 rocks. Movement along the fault, the break in the earth's crust, postdates or is younger than deposition of the horizontal cross-cut beds. How much younger is impossible to tell from Figure 4-1A, since there are no key horizons or beds above the fault which were not broken and which could establish a positive youngest date possible. The fault could have happened at any time after deposition of bed 3, the youngest bed cut by the fault.

Essentially the same relationships are shown in faulted beds in Figure 4-1B, but here, after displacement, the fault has been buried by younger horizontal rocks. The overlying layer has not been cut by the fault and hence is younger than the movement of the fault. Relationships shown in Figure 4-1B establish that the fault which cuts block A and B and which displaced the black horizontal bed followed deposition of the beds 1 to 3, but preceded accumulation of the sediments of bed 4 which

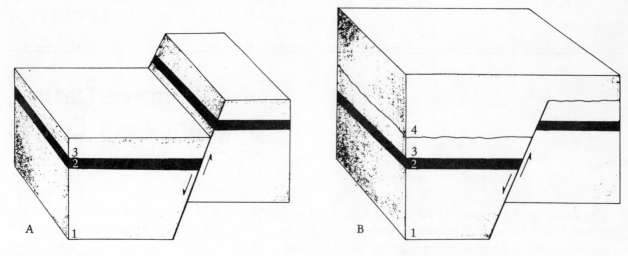

Figure 4-1. Block diagrams showing relationships of normal faulting. A. Relationships subsequent to faulting, but prior to deposition. B. Relationships after faulting and deposition which allow relative dating of the fault.

bury the fault. Movement along the fault is dated by cross-cutting and superposition relationships. Faults and folds can be dated in this general manner, by determination of the youngest rocks involved in the faulting and folding and of the oldest rocks which have not been involved in the movements.

Major unconformities, erosional breaks or loss of record, can be dated in the same manner. For example, beds 1 to 7 in Figure 4-2A were deposited then tilted or folded as shown in Figure 4-2B. The tilted edges were eroded to produce an erosional plane as shown in Figure 4-2C; the eroded surface was then buried with rock units 8 and 9 as shown in Figure 4-2D. Unit 8 rests on various rock units below the erosional surface or unconformity. On the left side of the block, unit 8 rests on beds 1 and 2, while on the right it rests on beds 6 and 7. Many beds have been removed on the left part of the block.

Erosion and formation of the unconformity must be pre-bed 8, of necessity, because bed 8 has buried the erosional surface, and has left debris of all formations from 1 through 7 strewn across the surface like crumbs on a cake platter. The youngest bed that can be seen below the unconformity in the diagram is bed 7, since by the Law of Superposition, 7 is the youngest bed of the sequence of 1 through 7 in Figure 4-2A. Therefore the period of erosion must have followed deposition of bed 7 but preceded deposition of bed 8. The erosional surface then would be dated as post-7 and pre-8.

Two other methods of relative dating can be illustrated in relationship to the character and thickness of the beds involved. In Figure 4-3A, the thickness of units 1 through 3 remain relatively constant from the left to the right side of the block diagram. However, unit 4 thins over the small fold in the central part of the diagram and thickens very markedly along the flanks of the fold. This relationship suggests that the folding began sometime during deposition of bed 4, because bed 3 and older units below are folded and the upper surface of bed 4 is relatively horizontal. Differences in thickness between the top and bottom of bed 4 indicate the amount of folding. Bed 5 is parallel to the upper surface of bed 4 and indicates that the minor folding was accomplished before deposition of unit 5. From thickness, alone, in fortunate circumstances, one can obtain some information on periods of deformation.

These examples, coupled with unconformities such as in Figure 4-3B, are the evidence for dating of the major periods of mountain building that have affected the continental borders of North America during the geologic past.

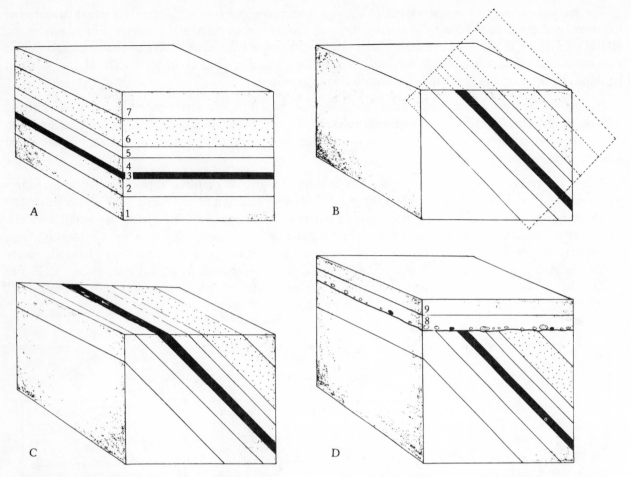

Figure 4-2. Block diagrams showing sequence of development of an angular unconformity. A. Deposition of beds 1 to 7. B. Tilting or folding of the sedimentary sequence. C. Erosion of the tilted beds to produce a horizontal surface. D. Burial of the eroded surface by deposition of beds 8 and 9 to produce the angular unconformity.

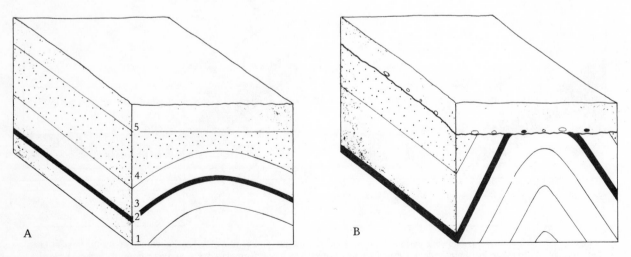

Figure 4-3. Block diagrams of two folded sedimentary sequences showing different methods of dating. A. Folding with contemporaneous deposition demonstrated by variations in thickness of bed 4 without evidence of erosion. B. Folded and eroded anticline which was subsequently buried by later deposition. Folding predated deposition of the overlying horizontal bed.

The nature of the sediments related to erosional surfaces and to fault scarps, or other features of relief, may also aid in defining the relative time of formation of particular features. For example, the clastic wedges of the Devonian Catskill delta or of the major Cretaceous belts of coarse conglomerate and sandstone in western North America effectively date the time of major uplift of the Acadian landmass in the east and the Laramide Mountains in the west.

Dating of intrusive igneous rocks is generally based upon the Principle of Cross-cutting Relationships. One can formulate a general rule and say that intrusive igneous masses are younger than the rocks they invade and older than the rocks that overlie them in a nonconformable or erosional relationship.

A lava flow and a horizontal sill or a sheet of intruded igneous material appear similar on maps but have quite different age relationships. Figure 4-4C shows the relationships seen with a lava flow. The rocks below are baked, shown by the stippled pattern, but the rocks above were deposited over the cooled lava surface. The upper surface may be irregular or it may be eroded to a nearly smooth plane, but debris of the lava commonly occurs in the basal part of the overlying sequence. Lava flows are dated like sedimentary layered rocks, using superposition. Relationships of a sill are shown in Figure 4-4D. The sill is shown as the irregularly margined mass with stippled baked zones in the enclosing

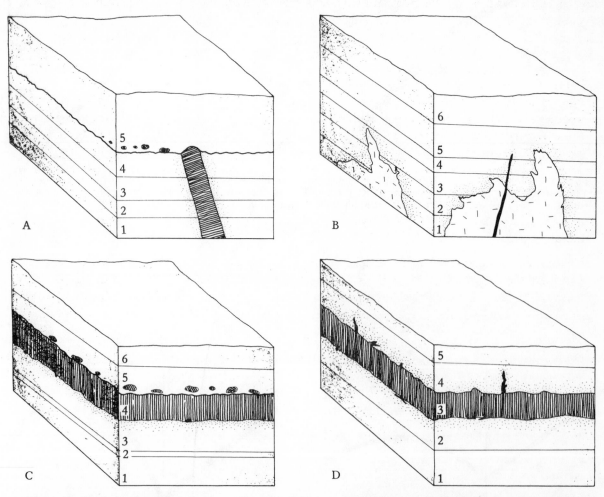

Figure 4-4. Block diagrams showing various relationships of igneous and sedimentary rocks which are useful in relative dating. A. A dike has intruded beds 1 through 4 but is overlain unconformably by a younger deposit, bed 5. Eroded remnants of the dike are included in the basal deposits of bed 5. B. Two intrusive igneous masses which cut and bake beds 1 through 5. The age relationships of bed 6 and the intrusive masses cannot be determined. C. A lava flow, bed 4, has baked part of bed 3 and has supplied erosional debris which is included in bed 5. The flow postdates bed 3 and predates bed 5. D. An igneous sill which has baked both the overlying and underlying beds is younger than any bed of the sequence.

subparallel beds. Country rock near the igneous mass shows zones of baking because of intrusion of the fluid melted rock material into the country rock. In contrast to lava flows, the country rock both above and below the sill have been baked. Minor fingers or apophyses of the igneous molten material have penetrated into the overlying and underlying rocks.

Dating of some igneous intrusive masses may pose other problems as well in instances where the melt has not penetrated to the surface. Cross-cutting relationships date the mass only as younger than the youngest rocks effected by the heat or by the intrusive mass. This type of relationship is shown in Figure 4-4B where two intrusive masses cut through rock sequences 1 through 5 but have not affected the rocks above bed 5. Both intrusive masses can be dated only as post-bed 5. The small black dike postdates the larger intrusive which it cuts. A younger limit cannot be definitely established for either.

Compare this with Figure 4-4A where the igneous mass was intruded, then exposed during a period of erosion, and then buried by sediments deposited above the unconformity. In this instance, beds 1 through 4 have been affected by the intrusive mass, but unit 5 above has not been affected. Eroded fragments of the intrusive dike have been incorporated into the base of unit 5 as well. Dating of the intrusive can be established in a manner similar to that of the cross-cutting relationships seen earlier in Figure 4-1. Formation of the intrusive in this instance is post-bed 4 and pre-bed 5. The time span between beds 4 and 5 may be great and without other methods, such as will be studied in the exercise on geochronometry, precision of relative dating is sometimes limited.

Procedure

1. Using these dating techniques, determine the sequence of geologic events for each of the blocks in Figures 6-5A to G. Write the histories in list form, with the oldest at the bottom numbered 1, and youngest at the top. In general the blocks are arranged from those with the simplest histories to those with the most complex histories. Begin with block A and work toward the more complex blocks. Relationships which are not immediately evident can be most easily interpreted by working from the surface down, or by working backwards through time, starting with the youngest event and proceeding down into the geologic history recorded earlier in the blocks. Keep in mind the Principles of Original Horizontality, Cross-cutting Relationships, and Superposition, as well as the evidences afforded by sedimentary character, and by the degree of folding or metamorphism.

Unconformities are shown by thick wavey lines, faults are shown by relatively thick lines. Erosional debris of older material is shown by symbols suggesting boulders or cobbles of older material in overlying sedimentary sequences. Intrusive contacts are generally shown with a toothed or sharply serrated margin where appropriate.

The upper surfaces of several blocks show details or relationships which may not be evident in cross-sections on the side of the block. In this same sense, a geologic map may show relationships which have relative time significance, which may not be visible in one of the cross-sections along the margin.

2. The last block, Figure 4-5H, shows several relationships which are impossible. Locate the errors and explain why the relationships are not possible.

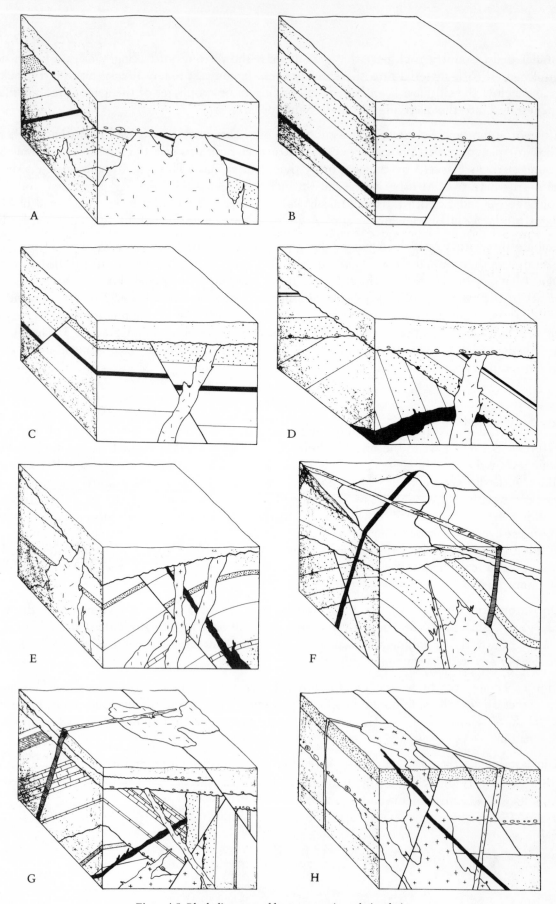

Figure 4-5. Block diagram problems concerning relative dating.

44

Geochronometry

1. On Figure 5-1 plot and label a decay curve for parent atoms and a growth curve for daughter atoms. Begin with P_0 parents and 0 daughters. How do these curves differ from a curve that represents sand flowing through an hour glass?

2. On Figure 5-2 plot a curve representing the ratio of daughter atoms to parent atoms (D/P) with time in half-lives.

3. Mica from unit J in Figure 5-4 contains an Ar^{40} to K^{40} ratio of 4 to 1. K^{40} to Ar^{40} has a half-life of 1.3 b.y. Using your curve in Figure 5-2 find the apparent age of J.

4. Feldspar from unit K (granite) has the same Ar^{40}/K^{40} as unit J, yet field relations suggest that one unit is older than the other. List possible reasons for this.

5. Uranium samples 1, 2, 3 were collected from different exposures of Unit L (diorite). Plot and label each of these samples on Figure 5-3 (Concordia curve). Which sample by itself indicates a reliable age?

Pb^{206}/U^{238} (half-life = 4.5 b.y.)	Pb^{207}/U^{235} (half-life = 0.71 b.y.)
Sample 1: 0.29	7.5
Sample 2: 0.42	12.5
Sample 3: 0.36	10.0

6. On Figure 5-3 construct a straight line through the points representing samples 1, 2, 3. Note that both ends of this line intersect the Concordia curve. One intersection indicates the time when the atomic clock was first set; the other indicates when lead was lost from the system at a later time, perhaps during a geologic event. Is it necessary to find a sample that has not lost lead to get a reliable age?

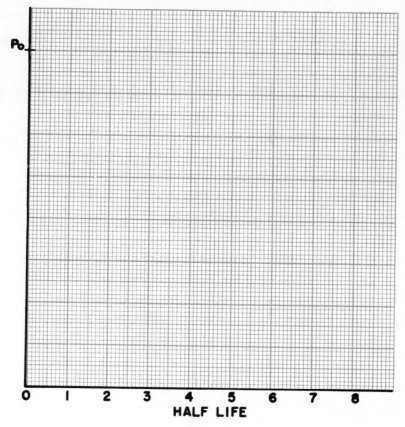

Figure 5-1.

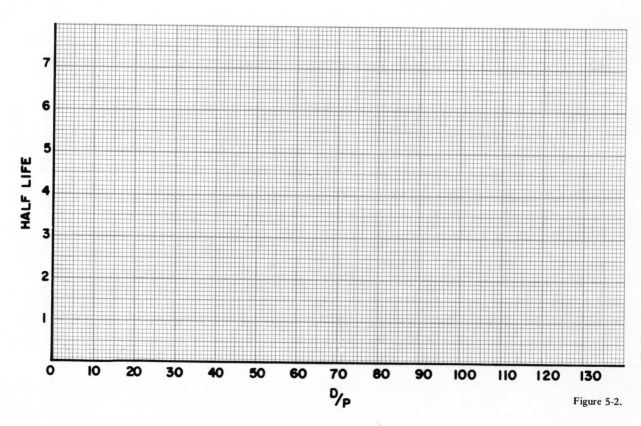

Figure 5-2.

46

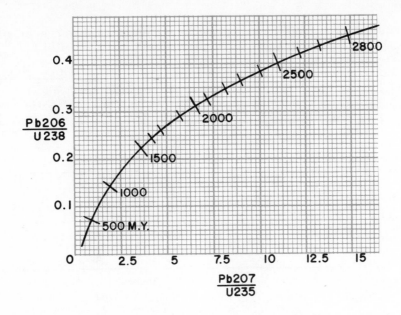

Figure 5-3. Concordia curve.

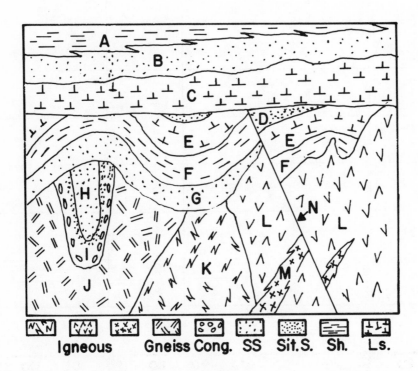

Figure 5-4.

47

7. Determine the sequence of lettered geological events in Figure 5-4. Arrange these in the table below starting with the oldest event at the top.

Event	Older than	Because	Younger than	Because

B contains a Tertiary mammal fauna.
C contains Jurassic ammonites.
D, E, F, G, is a conformable sequence.
I contains a basal conglomerate with clasts derived from J and K.

Ohio Fossils

Materials: Set of common Ohio fossils, and *Ohio Fossils* by A. La Rocque and M.F. Marple, Ohio Geological Survey Bulletin 54.

Box I contains a clam, snail, nautiloid, bryozoan, and corals.

Box II contains assorted brachiopods. These animals are figured and discussed in *Ohio Fossils*.

1. To what phylum and class does the nautiloid belong? What do the rings around the specimen represent?

2. What type of preservation does the snail demonstrate?

3. Refer to the clam and a brachiopod. Which has identical valves? Which has symmetrical valves?

4. Clam shells open automatically due to the elasticity of a ligament at the hingeline; the clam is open when at rest. Most brachiopod valves are opened by contraction of a pair of diductor muscles, and so work is performed to keep the valves open. How do these two different valve mechanisms affect the way clams and brachiopods are preserved?

5. Identify the corals using *Ohio Fossils*. Which specimen represents colonial organisms?

6. Identify the genus and age of each brachiopod in Box II.

Trilobite Biostratigraphy

Materials: Trilobite casts of specimens similar to those illustrated on Plates 1 and 2 are obtainable from Junipera Mountains Cultural Center, 7621 Highway 60, Riverside, California 92509.

Trilobites are extinct arthropods that are characterized by a longitudinally three-lobed carapace that is divided transversely into distinct regions termed cephalon (head), thorax, and pygidium (tail). Examples of unusually good preservation have demonstrated the presence of numerous ventral appendages including antennae. Important morphologic features are illustrated below.

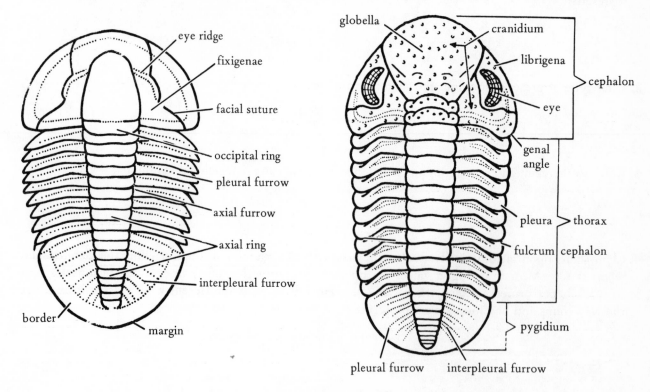

Figure 7-1. *Olenellus* (left) and *Phacops* (right) from *Treatise on Invertebrate Paleontology, Arthropoda 1.*

1. The casts in the study set are replicas of whole trilobites, some of which are from the best of known specimens. It is much more common to find one of the three main parts of the carapace than whole specimens. Does each trilobite fossil necessarily represent the death on an animal? Explain.

2. Compare some of the trilobites in the study set with Figure 7-1 to see if you can distinguish some of the important features. Do all of the specimens have eyes?

3. What characteristics of trilobites make them excellent guide fossils for Cambrian and Ordovician rocks?

4. Using Plates 1 and 2, identify the genus and age of each of the trilobite casts in the study set. Specimens are numbered on the back.

Genus	Age Range
1. _____	_____
2. _____	_____
3. _____	_____
4. _____	_____
5. _____	_____
6. _____	_____
7. _____	_____
8. _____	_____
9. _____	_____
10. _____	_____
11. _____	_____
12. _____	_____
13. _____	_____
14. _____	_____

CAMBRIAN TRILOBITES

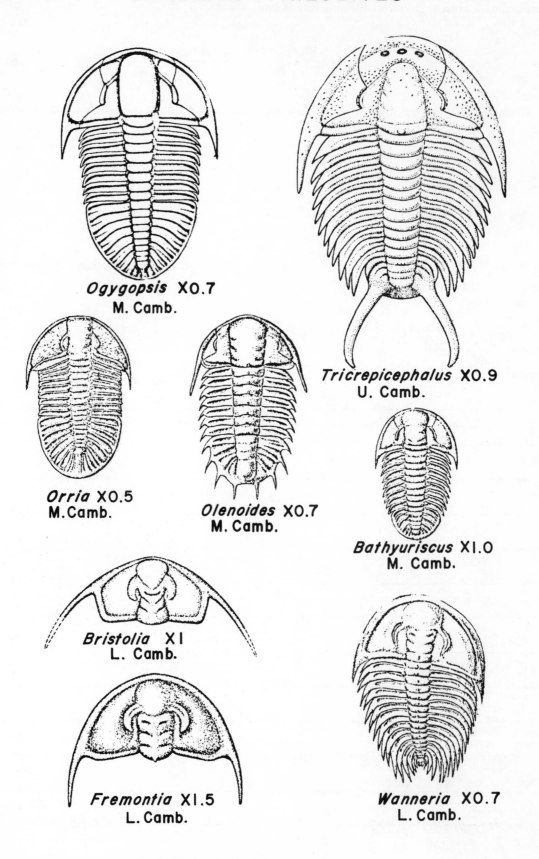

Ogygopsis X0.7
M. Camb.

Tricrepicephalus X0.9
U. Camb.

Orria X0.5
M.Camb.

Olenoides X0.7
M. Camb.

Bathyuriscus X1.0
M. Camb.

Bristolia X1
L. Camb.

Fremontia X1.5
L. Camb.

Wanneria X0.7
L. Camb.

ORDOVICIAN——DEVONIAN TRILOBITES

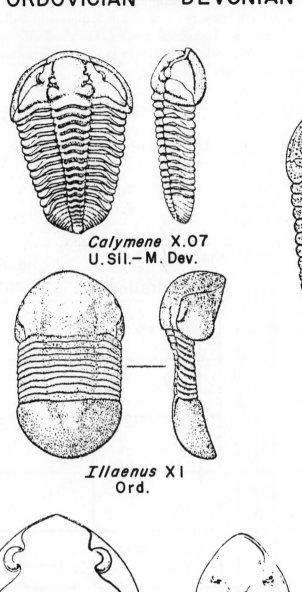

Calymene X.07
U. Sil.— M. Dev.

Illaenus X1
Ord.

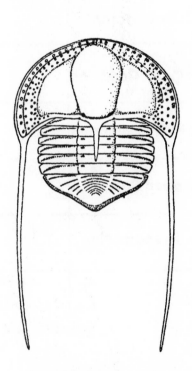

Phacops X1.2
Sil.- Dev.

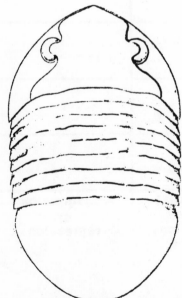

Homotelus X1.5
U. Ord.

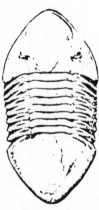

Isotelus X1
M.-U. Ord.

Cryptolithus X2.7
Ord.

5. Figure 7-2 illustrates four stratigraphic sections where examples of the trilobites you just identified were found. Numbers to the right of each section refer to the trilobites and indicate the stratigraphic horizon at which specimens were found. Lithologic symbols are standard; the wavy pattern at the base of each section represents metamorphic rock. Heavy horizontal lines represent formational contacts; wavy horizontal lines indicate angular discordance.

a. In each section in Figure 7-2 mark the approximate location of the boundaries between the following time-stratigraphic units: Lower, Middle, and Upper Cambrian, and Ordovician, Silurian, and Devonian.

b. Correlate the sections in Figure 7-2 by connecting the time-stratigraphic boundaries. Indicate unconformities with a heavy line.

c. Reconstruct the geological history of this region by completing the blanks in the table below.

Geologic Age	Event	sections involved				Position of Shoreline	Land-Sea Trend
		1	2	3	4		
Devonian							
Silurian							
Ordovician							
Upper Cambrian							
Middle Cambrian							
Lower Cambrian							
Precambrian							
	erosion or deposition	check answers				relative to sections	transgression or regression

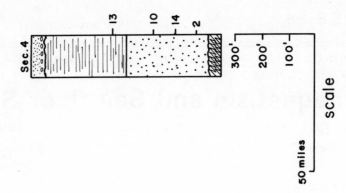

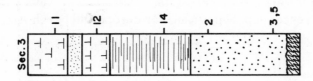

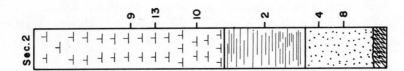

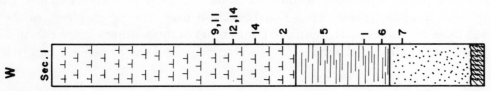

Figure 7-2.

55

EXERCISE 8

Paleomagnetism and Sea-floor Spreading

Materials: Jigsaw pieces of the southern continents marked with paleomagnetically determined latitudes for the Jurassic. Transform fault model of sea-floor spreading described by W.S. Mc Loda in Journal of Geological Education, vol. 17, no. 4, 1969.

1. Assuming the data in Figure 8-1 are accurate, what are two ways to explain the changing pole positions and the differences in pole positions for Europe and North America at any one time?

2. On the coordinates in Figure 8-2 plot a curve showing the amount of relative difference in pole positions between North America and Europe with time. For an accurate curve you would require great circle distances, but for the purposes of this lab consider the apparent distances from Figure 8-1.

3. Assuming that differences in pole positions are due to continental drift, at what time does your curve on Figure 8-2 suggest that North America and Europe were closest together? Explain.

4. Paleomagnetic data indicate the former direction of the north magnetic pole and its latitudinal distance (inclination), but no information regarding longitude is available. If you do not understand the reasons for this, ask your lab instructor to demonstrate this concept with a compass.

   In reconstructing the former positions of continents, paleomagnetic data are inconclusive without other geological data. However, any reconstruction must agree with paleomagnetically determined latitudes insofar as they are correct. Paleomagnetic data as well as glacial, paleontologic, geological data are part of a puzzle with many possible variables that must fit together to give a consistent picture. Try your hand at reconstructing Gondwanaland using the jigsaw pieces of the southern continents; if these are not available, cut out the outlines of the southern continents in Figure 8-3. Constraints to your model are the shapes of the continents and the paleomagnetically determined latitudes.

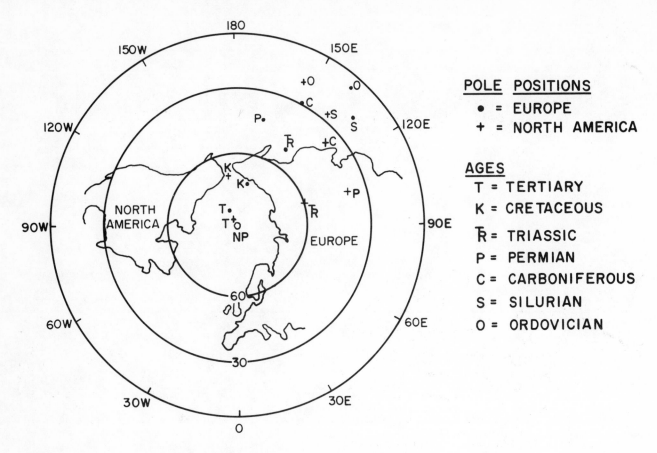

Figure 8-1. Polar equal-area projection of the northern hemisphere with average pole positions determined by paleomagnetic studies (data from *Paleomagnetism and its application to geological and geophysical problems* by E. Irving, Wiley, 1964).

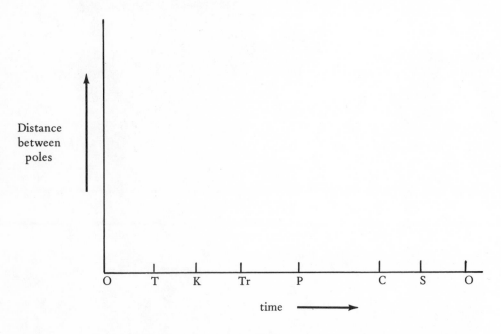

Figure 8-2.

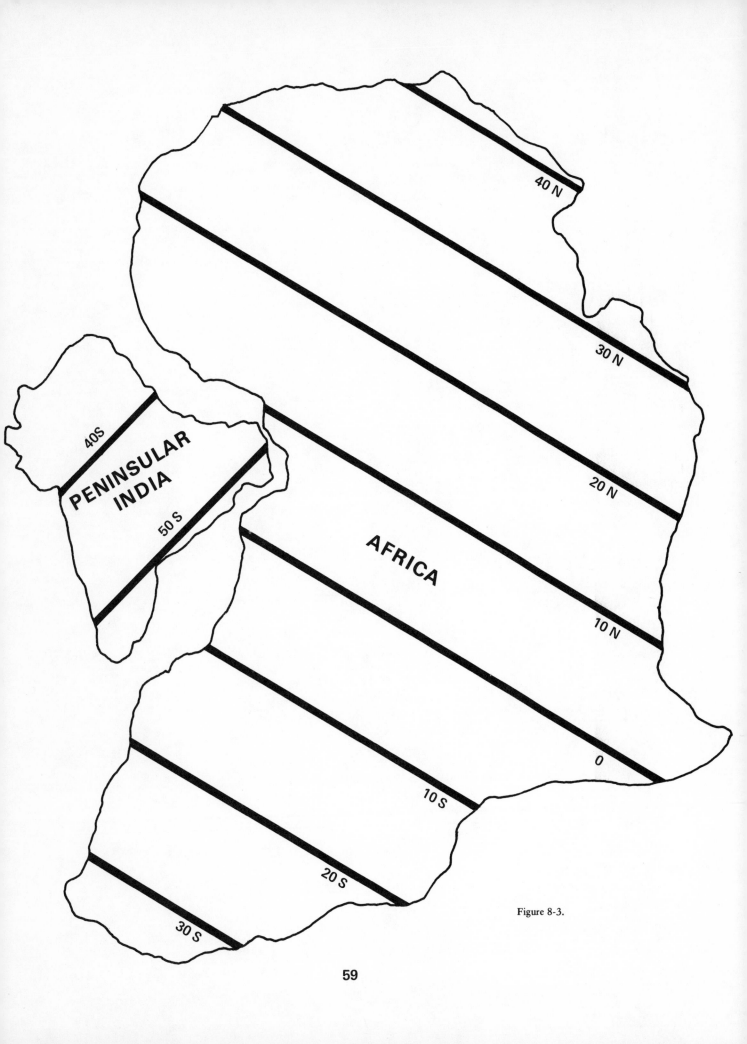

40 N

30 N

20 N

10 N

0

10 S

20 S

30 S

40S

50 S

PENINSULAR INDIA

AFRICA

Figure 8-3.

59

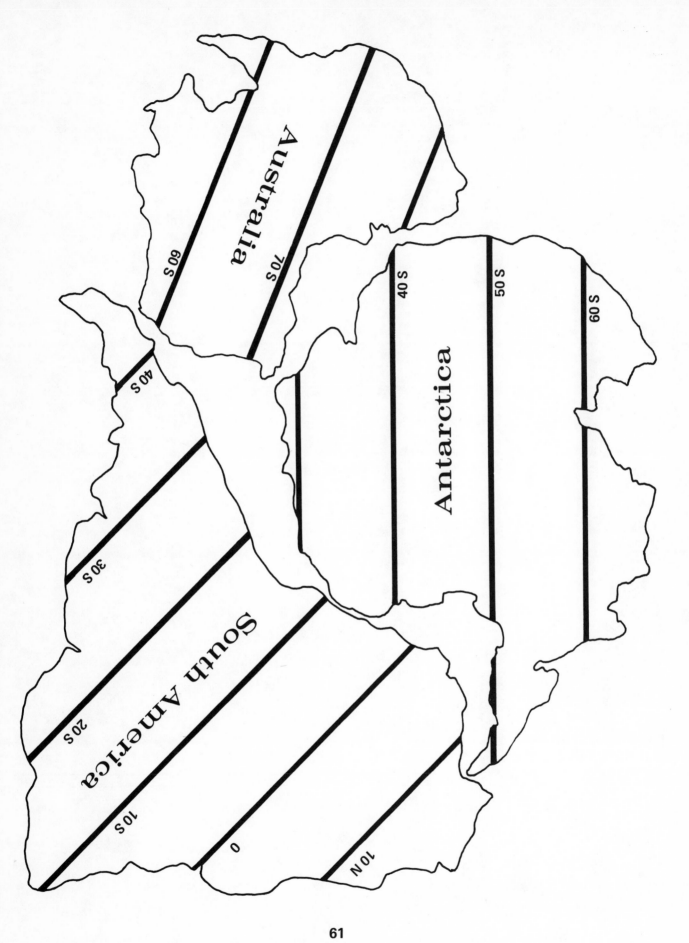

61

5. Ask your lab instructor to demonstrate the sea-floor spreading model. Work with this model until you fully understand it, particularly the concept of transform faults.

6. Figure 8-4 illustrates a diagrammatic mid-ocean ridge system and transform fault. The cross-hatched bars represent negative magnetic anomalies measured on the ocean floor.

    a. Using the paleomagnetic time scale (Fig. 8-5), label each epoch and event on the magnetic anomaly map of the ocean floor (Fig. 8-4).

    b. Calculate the rate of sea-floor spreading in cm/year. Does the rate remain constant during the last 3.6 million years?

    c. If Figure 8-4 represents part of the Mid-Atlantic Ridge at a point where the Atlantic is now 6,000 km across, how long ago did the split occur? Does your answer agree with the geological data?

    d. On the basis of the magnetic anomalies on the ocean floor, extend the reversal time scale on Figure 8-5 back beyond the Gilbert Epoch as far as possible. How would you go about proving that the extended time scale is accurate and that it is not based on a changing rate of spreading?

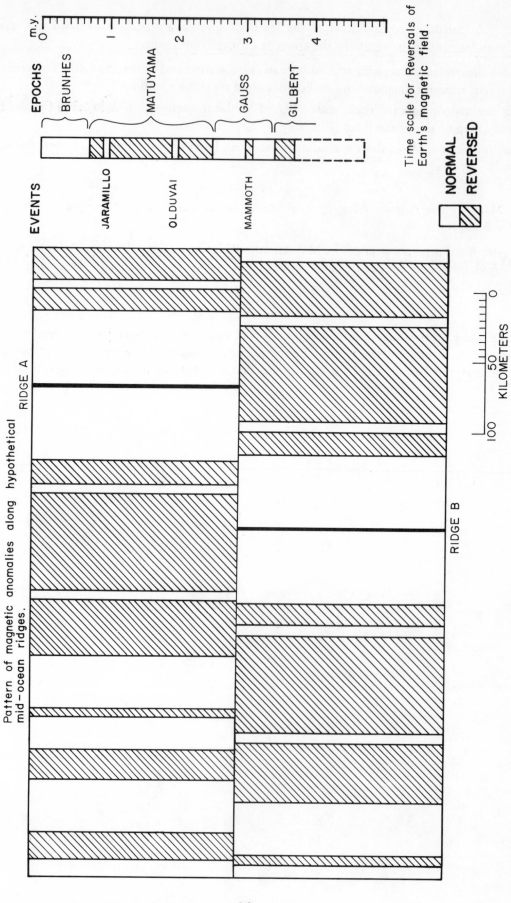

Pattern of magnetic anomalies along hypothetical mid-ocean ridges.

RIDGE A

RIDGE B

KILOMETERS

EPOCHS

BRUNHES

MATUYAMA

GAUSS

GILBERT

EVENTS

JARAMILLO

OLDUVAI

MAMMOTH

m.y.

Time scale for Reversals of Earth's magnetic field.

NORMAL

REVERSED

Figure 8-4.

Figure 8-5.

64

Ocean Floors

Materials: Maps of the Pacific, Atlantic, and Indian ocean floors (available from the National Geographic Society).

1. Suggest one or more hypotheses for the origin of the following features of the ocean floors:

   a. Abyssal Plains.

   b. Mississippi Cone in the Gulf of Mexico.

   c. Laurentian Cone south of Newfoundland.

d. Salt domes in the Gulf of Mexico (Sigsbee Knolls on Atlantic map).

e. Rift valleys on continents and mid-ocean ridges.

2. Why is the Amazon Cone considerably north of the mouth of the Amazon River?

3. It is hypothesized that Iceland is part of the Mid-Atlantic Ridge. What are the pros and cons of this hypothesis?

4. According to sea-floor spreading theory the ages of oceanic islands should be older in proportion to their distance from a mid-ocean ridge. Listed below are several islands in the Atlantic Ocean with the ages of the oldest rocks found on each of them. Calculate a rough estimate of the rate of spreading in each case.

Island	Distance (1 mi $\cong$ 60,000 in.)	Age	Rate in/yr.
Tristan da Cunha (37°S, 13°W),	_____	1 m.y.	_____
Ascension (8°S, 14°W)	_____	1 m.y.	_____
Fernando de Noronha (4°S, 32°W)	_____	120 m.y.	_____
Sao Tone (0°, 7°E)	_____	120 m.y.	_____
Cape Verde (17°N, 25°W)	_____	150 m.y.	_____
Canary (27°N, 15°W)	_____	32 m.y.	_____
Azores (38°N, 28°W)	_____	20 m.y.	_____
Bermuda (33°N, 28°W)	_____	36 m.y.	_____

5. What are some of the possible reasons for inconsistencies in the above results?

6. List some promising places to search for the oldest oceanic rocks.

7. The island of Hawaii is currently the only active volcano in the Hawaiian chain. The islands to the west have progressively more ancient volcanoes. Suggest one or more hypotheses to explain this phenomenon.

8. Suggest several promising places to search for oil beneath the oceans.

9. Explain the presence of the Aleutian Islands.

10. Africa is almost completely surrounded by mid-oceanic ridges and rift areas. Explain how the ocean floors can be spreading toward Africa from all directions.

11. What evidence can you find that Africa is breaking up?

12. Suggest an origin for the formation of the Himalayas.

13. On Figure 9-1 construct a rough cross-section from the Fiji Islands (18°S, 178°E) through Santiago, Chile, to Capetown, South Africa. Illustrate and label the following features: convection systems, lithosphere, asthenosphere, mid-ocean ridges, volcanic areas, shallow and deep earthquake areas, high and low heat flow areas.

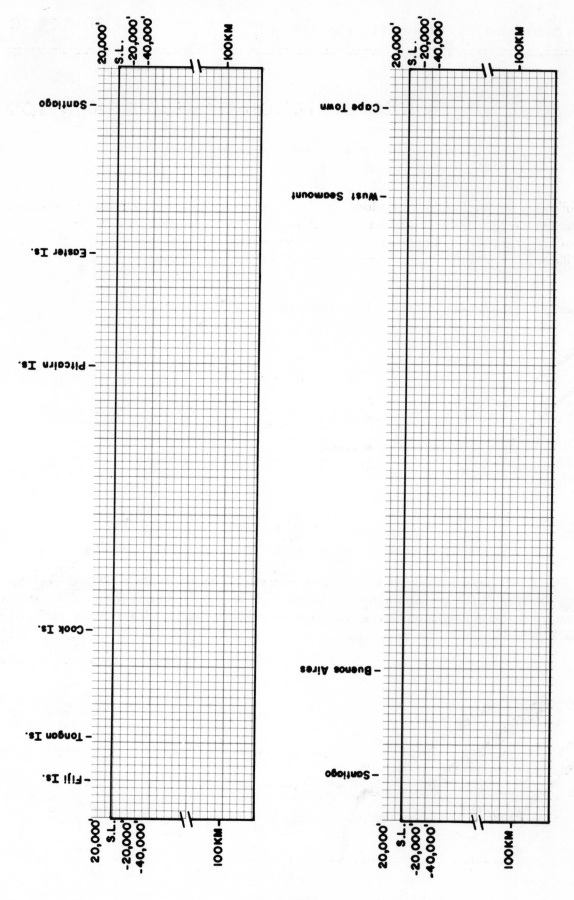

Figure 9-1.

70

Interpretation of Geologic Maps

The following is a set of rules with block diagram illustrations which will aid in the interpretation and understanding of geologic maps. As you examine these block diagrams, realize that the upper surface of the diagram corresponds to the view shown by a geologic map, whereas the sides of the diagram illustrate the third dimension which the student must visualize from only the map view.

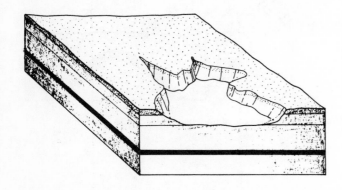

Figure 10-1. Horizontal beds have a broad continuous outcrop pattern which will parallel the contour lines.

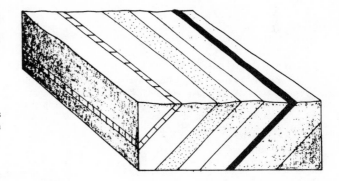

Figure 10-2. Dipping strata will be expressed on a map as stripes, with the youngest strata in the direction of dip in a normal sequence.

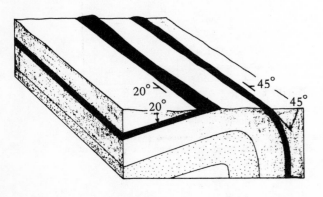

Figure 10-3. For a stratum of constant thickness, the outcrop pattern will broaden with a decrease in dip and shorten with an increase in dip. The strike and dip directions of the beds are shown by the "T-shaped" symbol. The dip angle is measured in degrees.

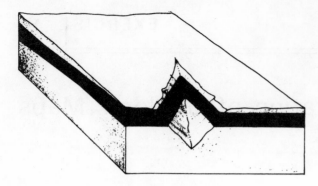

Figure 10-4. As strata intersect stream valleys, the beds will form a "V" pattern with the "V" pointing in the direction of dip. An exception to this occurs when the dip of the bed is less that the slope angle.

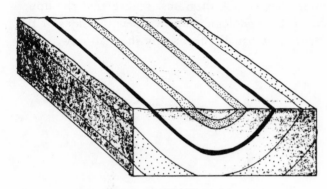
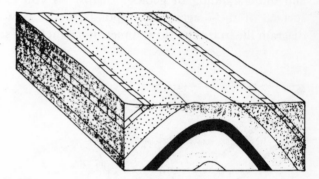

Figure 10-5, A and B. Anticlines and synclines whose axes are horizontal are called horizontal folds. Horizontal folds will have a parallel outcrop pattern on a map.

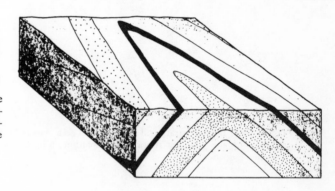

Figure 10-6. Folds whose axes are inclined to the horizontal are called plunging. Plunging folds have converging or diverging outcrop patterns. The outcrop pattern of a plunging anticline will close, or "V," in the direction of plunge.

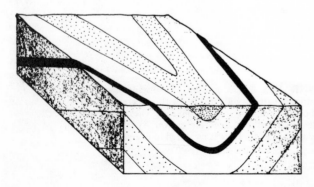

Figure 10-7. The outcrop patterns of plunging synclines open in the direction of plunge.

The youngest beds will be exposed in the center of a syncline. The oldest beds are exposed in the center of an anticline.

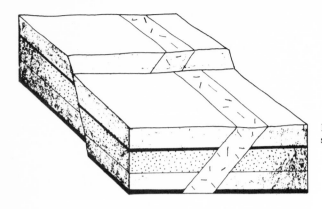

Figure 10-8. Abrupt breaks in the outcrop patterns are surface expressions of faults.

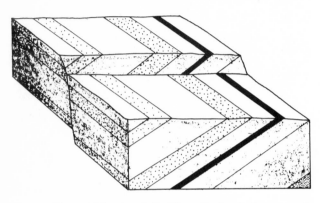

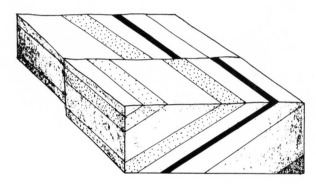

Figure 10-9, A and B. When dipping beds are cut by faults, there is apparent lateral shift in the outcrop pattern toward the direction of dip on the upthrown block.

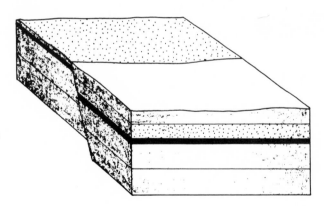

Figure 10-10. Across any fault trace, the oldest beds will be exposed on the upthrown block.

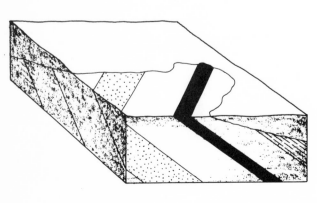

Figure 10-11. The outcrop pattern of nearly horizontal beds superimposed on the striped outcrop pattern of dipping beds indicates an **angular unconformity.**

73

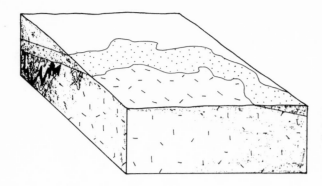

Figure 10-12. Unaltered sedimentary formations directly overlying an intrusive igneous rock mass indicates a nonconformity.

Figure 10-13. The irregular outcrop pattern indicating an ancient erosion surface enclosed by parallel formations with rocks of intervening ages missing illustrates a disconformity.

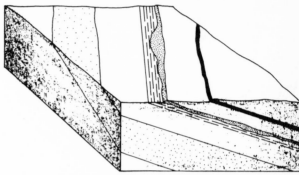

Procedure

The following two pages of block diagrams (Figures 10-14 and 10-15) are for student practice. The first page has partially completed diagrams which the student is to complete. The second page of block diagrams are to be completed by the student according to instructions given by the instructor.

Geologic cross-sections can be made from geologic maps by the following procedure:

1. Overlay a strip of paper along the specified section-line on the geologic map.
2. Mark on the overlay strip the point of intersection of all formation contacts and faults.
3. Determine from the map the direction and angle of dip of each formation, and fault and project the contacts at that dip angle for approximately one-quarter inch.
4. Connect the projected lines into anticlines or synclines. Interrupt the pattern at the intersection of fault planes.

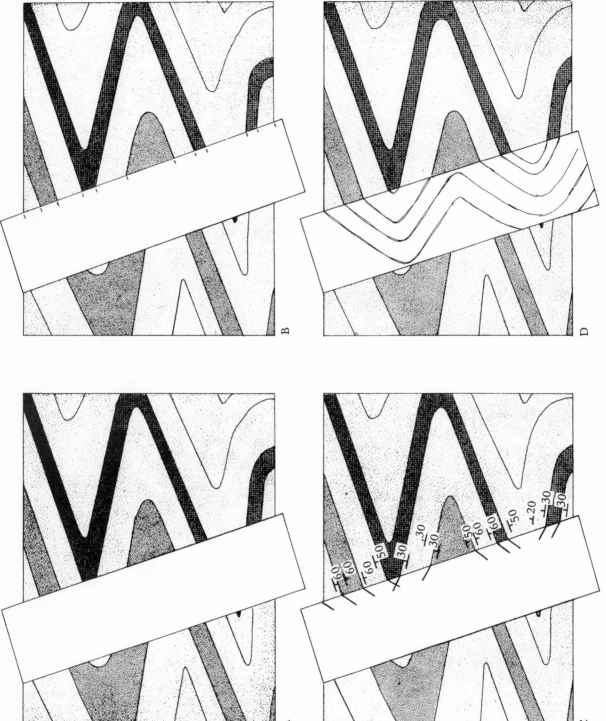

Figure 10-14. Diagrams showing the procedure to be followed in construction of a geologic cross-section from map data.

75

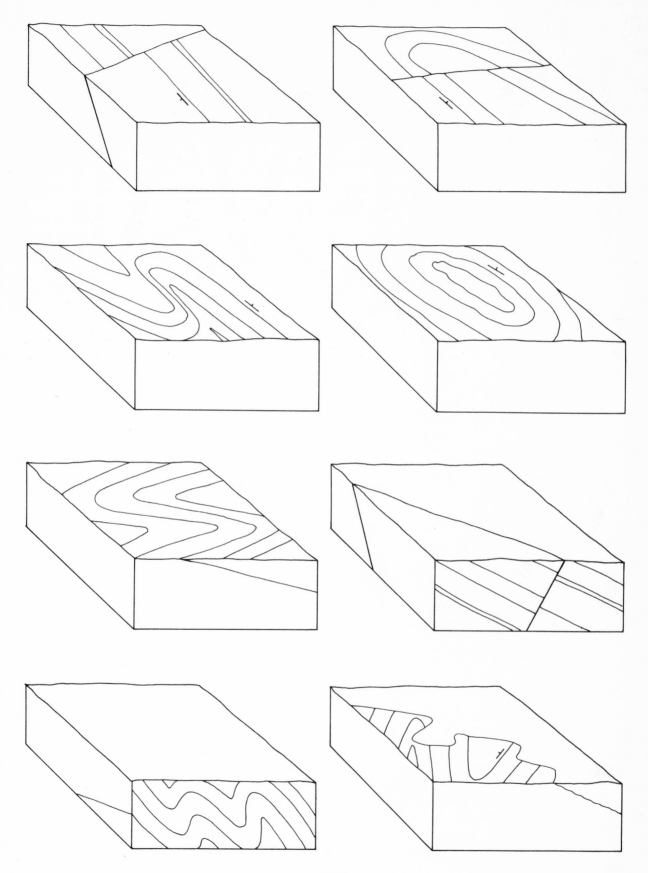

Figure 10-15.

Figure 10-16.

EXERCISE 11

Geologic Map of Ohio

1. Why is the Mississippian-Pennsylvanian contact so irregular?

2. What is the age of the rock exposed at the highest point in Ohio (Logan County)?

3. What is the structure trending from the southwest corner of Ohio to the western tip of Lake Erie?

4. Estimate the strike and dip of beds in Franklin County. Devonian strata here are about 700 feet thick.

5. In Figure 11-1 construct a diagrammatic cross section from the northwest corner of Ohio to the southeast corner of Belmont County on the Ohio River.

NW

SE

Figure 11-1.

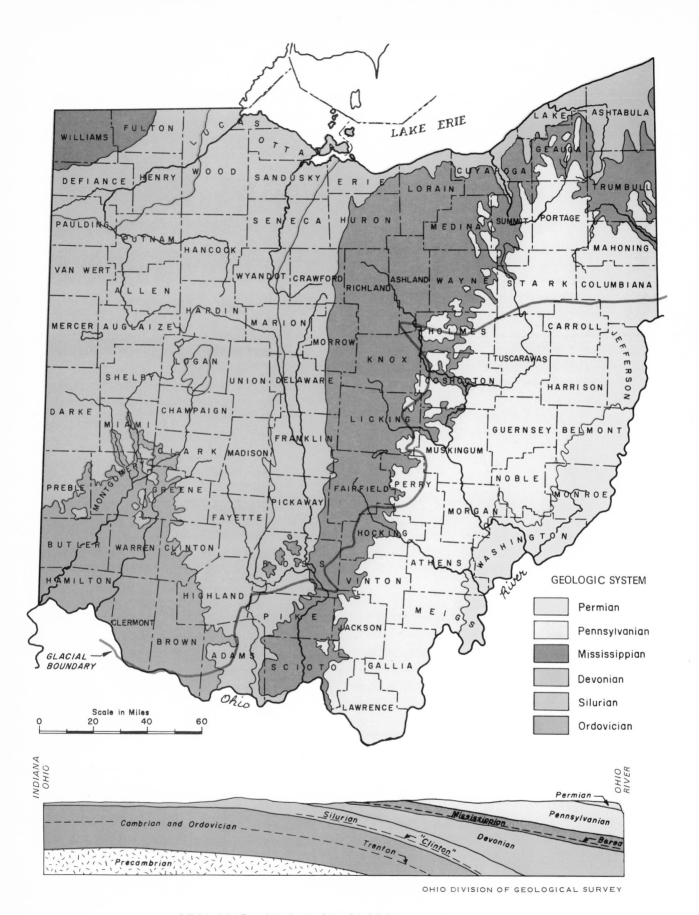

LAKE ERIE

WILLIAMS FULTON LUCAS OTTA
DEFIANCE HENRY WOOD SANDUSKY ERIE LORAIN CUYAHOGA LAKE ASHTABULA GEAUGA TRUMBULL
PAULDING PUTNAM SENECA HURON MEDINA SUMMIT PORTAGE MAHONING
VAN WERT ALLEN HANCOCK WYANDOT CRAWFORD RICHLAND ASHLAND WAYNE STARK COLUMBIANA
MERCER AUGLAIZE HARDIN MARION MORROW KNOX HOLMES CARROLL JEFFERSON
LOGAN UNION DELAWARE COSHOCTON TUSCARAWAS HARRISON
SHELBY CHAMPAIGN LICKING GUERNSEY BELMONT
DARKE MIAMI CLARK MADISON FRANKLIN MUSKINGUM NOBLE MONROE
PREBLE MONTGOMER GREENE PICKAWAY FAIRFIELD PERRY MORGAN
BUTLER WARREN CLINTON FAYETTE RO SS HOCKING ATHENS WASHINGTON
HAMILTON HIGHLAND VINTON MEIGS
CLERMONT BROWN ADAMS PIKE JACKSON GALLIA

GLACIAL
BOUNDARY

SCIOTO LAWRENCE

River

Ohio

Scale in Miles
0 20 40 60

GEOLOGIC SYSTEM

Permian
Pennsylvanian
Mississippian
Devonian
Silurian
Ordovician

INDIANA
OHIO

OHIO
RIVER

Permian

Cambrian and Ordovician   Silurian   Mississippian   Pennsylvanian

Trenton   "Clinton"   Devonian   Berea

Precambrian

OHIO DIVISION OF GEOLOGICAL SURVEY

GEOLOGIC MAP AND CROSS SECTION OF OHIO

Regional Geology of the United States

Materials: Geology map of the U.S. (Sheet 74 of the National Atlas published by the U.S. Geological Survey). Tectonic features map of the U.S. (Sheet 70 of the National Atlas).

1. In the spaces provided below describe the structure, ages, and depositional setting (platform or geosynclinal) of rocks in each province.

Province	Structure	Ages	Depositional Setting
Interior lowlands	e.g. Flat-lying rocks, a few normal faults	Upper, middle, and lower Paleozoic	Platform
Appalachian Plateau			
Ridge and Valley (Newer Appalachians)			

Blue Ridge (western margin of Older Appalachians)			
Piedmont (eastern part of older Appalachians)			
New England			
Gulf and East Coastal Plain			
Ouachita Mountains			

Great Plains			
Southern Rockies			
Northern Rockies			
Colorado Plateau			
Great Basin			

Columbia Plateau			
Sierra Nevada (eastern California)			
Pacific Coast Ranges			

2. How deep is the basement in the Michigan Basin? How does the surface map of the geology express the presence of this basin?

3. Where is the center of the Illinois Basin and how deep is it?

4. How does the geological map reflect the presence of the Ozark Dome? What kinds of evidence would you look for to establish whether it originated before, during, or after deposition of the overlying rocks?

5. Seismic studies suggest sediments are slowly slipping seaward into the Gulf of Mexico. What evidence can you find for this on the maps?

6. Newspapers have recently reported a controversy about whether or not part of California including Los Angeles is about to slide into the Pacific Ocean. What features do you see on the maps that might be behind these reports? What is happening to California?

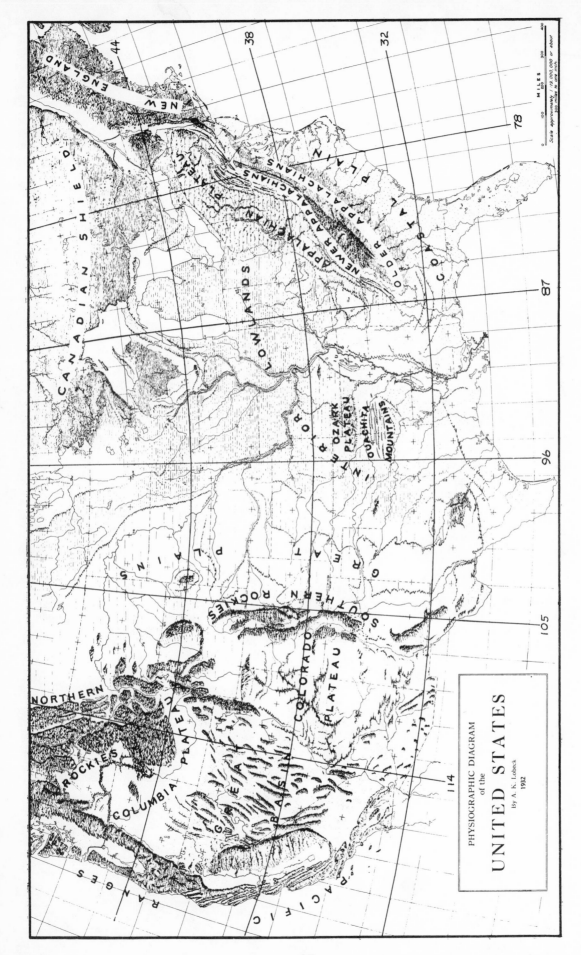

CANADIAN SHIELD

NEW ENGLAND

LOWLANDS

OLDER APPALACHIANS

NEWER APPALACHIANS

COASTAL PLAIN

INTERIOR

OZARK PLATEAU

OUACHITA MOUNTAINS

PLAINS

GREAT

SOUTHERN ROCKIES

COLORADO PLATEAU

NORTHERN

ROCKIES

COLUMBIA PLATEAU

GREAT BASIN

PACIFIC RANGES

PHYSIOGRAPHIC DIAGRAM
of the

UNITED STATES

By A. K. Lobeck
1932

MILES
100   200   300   400

Scale approximately 1:19,000,000 or about
300 miles to one inch

44

38

32

78

87

96

105

114

From the Lab Manual by Brice, 1962.

87

Canadian Shield-Core of the Continent

Geologic Map of North America
Scale: 1 inch = 80 miles

1. What are the ages and rock types on the north and south halves of the map area?

2. Draw an east-west geologic cross-section across the central part of the map from St. Paul, Minnesota, to Hamilton, Ontario.

3. Explain the isolated Cretaceous occurrences south of James Bay in the northeast corner of the map.

4. What are the geologic factors controlling the position and shape of Georgian and Green Bays?

Exercise 13

CANADIAN SHIELD

K	Light green	Cretaceous
Pz	Medium blue-gray	Paleozoic
IP_2	Blue and white, diagonal	Upper Pennsylvanian
IP_1	Blue	Lower Pennsylvanian
M_1	Lavender and red, diagonal	Mississippian
D	Brownish gray	Devonian
D_2	Brown	Upper Devonian
D_1	Brownish gray	Lower Devonian
S	Light purple	Silurian
O	Reddish purple	Ordovician
$\in$	Light orange-brown	Cambrian
p$\in$u	Yellowish tan	Upper Precambrian
p$\in$u$_2$	Reddish brown	Keweenawan sedimentary rocks
p$\in$u$_1$	Light brown	Keweenawan volcanic rocks
p$\in$b	Brownish green	Precambrian basic intrusives
p$\in$m	Light greenish brown	Middle Precambrian
p$\in$i	Pink	Precambrian granite and granite gneiss
p$\in$l	Olive green	Lower Precambrian

90

Interior Lowland-The Stable Interior

Geologic Map of North America (See Exercise 13)
Scale: 1 inch = 80 miles

1. What is the general structure in Michigan and Wisconsin?

2. Why are Ordovician, Silurian and Devonian rocks missing in the area east of Lake Superior?

EXERCISE 15

Folded Appalachian Mountains

Geologic Map of Pennsylvania
Scale: 1 inch = 4 miles

1. What is the likely source area for the Ordovician Martinsburg Formation and the Devonian Catskill Formation? With what geologic events are these associated?

2. Account for the difference in the structural patterns north and south of the Pennsylvania Turnpike which extends east-west through Carlisle, Pennsylvania?

3. Date the Appalachian folding in this area. Summarize the evidence.

4. Explain the origin and distribution of the igneous rocks in this area. With what episode of diastrophism are they associated?

5. What is the reason for the present course of the Susquehanna River cutting across the folds indiscriminately and across all different rock types?

94

Exercise 15

APPALACHIANS

TRIASSIC

ŦRd	Red diamonds and red lines	Dark gray igneous sills and dikes
ŦRlc		
ŦRg		Brunswick or Gettysburg Formation
ŦRb	Bright green with red patterns	Red sandstone and shale with minor conglomerate
ŦRh		
ŦRac		

PENNSYLVANIAN

IPp	Blue green	Pottsville Group
		Sandstone, conglomerate, shale and coals

MISSISSIPPIAN

Mmc	Pink	Mauch Chunk Formation
		Gray shale and red sandstone
Mp	Blue purple	Pocono Group
		Conglomerate, sandstone and shale

DEVONIAN

Dck	Orange	Catskill Formation
		Red sandstone and shale
Dm	Light orange	Marine beds, shale, sandstone, and limestone
Dho	Gray, green diagonals	Hamilton Group and Onendaga Formation,
		Shale, sandstone, and limestone
Doh	Orange and red diagonals	Oriskany and Helderberg Formations
		Fossiliferous sandstone and shale, and fossiliferous limestone

SILURIAN

Skt	Purple and blue diagonals	Keyser Formation and Tonoloway Formations
		Limestone
Sw	Dark and light blue, horizontal	Wills Creek Formation
		Shale and limestone with local sandstone
Sc	Light green, red stipples	Clinton Group
		Red iron-rich shale and sandstone
Sbm	Blue and purple, diagonal	Bloomsburg and McKenzie Formation
		Red to green shale and sandstone
St	Red and brown, diagonal	Tuscarora Formation
		Light coarse sandstone

ORDOVICIAN

Ojb	Orange and brown, diagonal	Juniata Formation and Bald Eagle Formation
		Red sandstone, shale and conglomerate
Om	Gray and pink, horizontal	Martinsburg Formation
		Marine shale
Oc		
Ohm	Blue grayish pink, diagonal	Chambersburg Formation, Hershey and Myerstown Formations
		Limestone
Osp	Light blue	St. Paul Group and Annville Formation
		Limestone with chert
Ob	Coarse pink and purple, diagonal	Beekmantown Group
		Limestone
Oor	Fine pink and purple, diagonal	Ontelaunee Formation, Epler Formation
		Rickenback Formation
		Limestone and dolomite
Os	Pink with blue, diagonals	Stonehenge Formation
		Limestone and limestone conglomerate

CAMBRIAN

Єc	Red and bright green, diagonal	Conococheague Group
		Limestone and dolomite
Єe	Grayish green, orange, crossed lines	Elbrook Formation
		Limestone and dolomite
Єwb	Green and orange vertical	Waynesboro Formation
		Red and purple shale with sandstone beds
Єt	Red and light green, diagonal	Tomstown Formation
		Dolomite, thin shaley beds
Єa	Pink and red squares	Antietam Formation
		Quartzite and schist
Єma	White and orange diagonals	
Єh	Orange and red verticals	Harpers Formation
		Phyllite and schist
Єwl	Pink and blue diagonals	Chickies Formation or Weverton Formation
		Quartzite and schist

IGNEOUS ROCKS

mr	Yellow, red dots	Metarhyolite
vs	Green, red stippled	Greenstone schist
mb	Brown, red stippled	Metabasalt

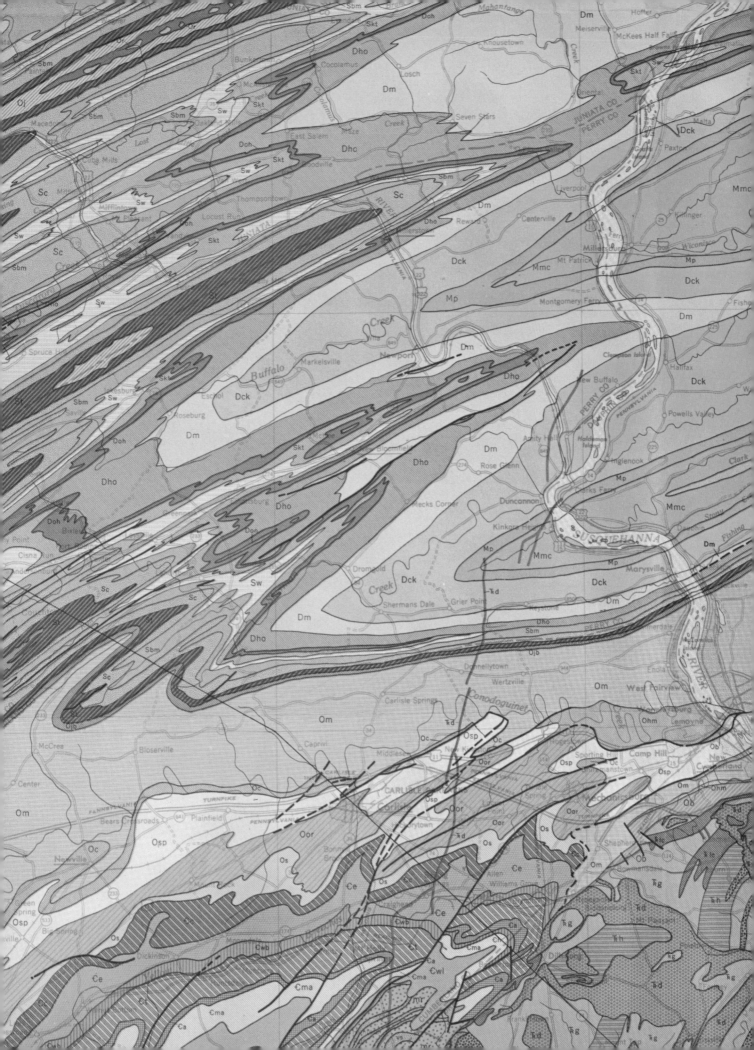

Colorado Plateau and Ancient Colorado Mountains

Geology of the Gateway Quad. Colorado

Scale: 1 inch = 2,000 feet (approximately .4 mile)

1. Draw a geologic cross-section along the diagonal line from the northeast corner to the south-central part of the map.

2. Note the unconformable contact between the Cutler Formation and the Precambrian gneiss and schist. The Cutler is missing in the northeast corner. Where exposed on the map, the Cutler Formation is conglomeratic. In light of these observations explain the origin of the Cutler Formation.

3. Explain the absence of the Moenkopi Formation beneath the Chinle Formation in the northeast corner of the map.

4. What is the structure of the Mesozoic rock units in the southern quarter of the map area?

5. Determine a sequence of events for the rock units in the map area. What is the age of the fault along Birch Creek?

Exercise 16

COLORADO PLATEAU

QUATERNARY

Qal	Stippled yellow	Alluvium
Qg	Green, yellow circles	Terrace gravels
Qfg	Dark yellow stipple	Angular fragments and boulders

CRETACEOUS

Kbc   Dark blue green diagonal   Burrow Canyon Formation

         Sandstone and conglomerate with interbedded
            green and purplish shale

JURASSIC

Jmb   Green horizontal   Morrison Formation

Jms   Solid blue green   Upper member of rusty red to grey shale
         Lower member of varicolored shale with
            buff sandstone and lenses of conglomerate

Js   Olive green, vertical   Summerville Formation
         Gray, green, and brown sandy shale and mudstone

Jec   Dark olive green, diagonal   Entrada Sandstone and Carmel Formation undivided
         Fine grained massive sandstone and red mudstone

Jn   Dark olive green, solid   Navajo Sandstone
         Buff, gray, crossbedded sandstone

Jk   Olive green, horizontal   Kayenta Formation
         Interbedded red, gray siltstone and sandstone

Jw   Dark olive, diagonal   Wingate Sandstone
         Massive reddish brown crossbedded sandstone

TRIASSIC

Ħc   Light blue, diagonal   Chinle Formation
         Red siltstone with lenses of red sandstone,
            shale, and conglomerate

Ħml   Dark blue, horizontal   Moenkopi Formation
         Sandy mudstone, brown and red with local gypsum

PENNSYLVANIAN

IPc   Medium blue, horizontal   Cutler Formation
         Red to purple conglomerate and sandstone

PRECAMBRIAN

p€   Brown and white, mottled   Gneiss, schist, granite, and pegmatite

Black Hills and High Plains

South Dakota State Geologic Map
Scale: 1 inch = 8 miles

1. What are the ages of the rocks shown on the map?

2. What geologic structure is represented by the belted elliptical outcrops?

3. What kind of rocks are exposed in the core of the Black Hills, along the flank, and in the plains to the east?

4. What is the age of the uplift that produced the Black Hills?

5. Locate and describe a nonconformity, disconformity, and two angular unconformities on the map. What is the age of each unconformity?

6. Where would be the most likely area in the Black Hills for commercial mineral production?

Exercise 17

SOUTH DAKOTA STATE GEOLOGIC MAP

TERTIARY

    Tw   Light yellow   White River Group

CRETACEOUS

    Kp   Light green, horizontal   Pierre Shale
    Kn   Light green, vertical   Niobrara Formation
    Kc   Light green, solid   Carlile Shale
    Kg   Light green, solid   Greenhorn Limestone
    Kbm   Light green, horizontal   Belle Fourche and Mowry Shales
    Ksi   Green, fine vertical   Skull Creek Shale, Inyan Kara Group

JURASSIC

    Jm   Grayish green   Morrison Formation
    Js   Grayish green, horizontal   Sundance Formation

TRIASSIC

    T s   Blue green, diagonal   Spearfish Formation

PERMIAN

    Pm   Blue, solid   Minnekahta and Opeche Formations

PENNSYLVANIAN

    Cm   Light blue, fine horizontal   Minnelua Sandstone

MISSISSIPPIAN

    Cp   Light blue, diagonal   Pahasapa Limestone and Englewood Limestone

ORDOVICIAN

    Ow   Purple   Whitewood Limestone

CAMBRIAN

    Єd   Orange brown   Deadwood Formation

PRECAMBRIAN

    pЄq   Dark brown   Granite and pegmatite
    pЄa   Dark brown   Basic igneous intrusions
    pЄsq   Light brown, horizontal
                    White irregular dashes   Schist and quartz
    pЄsc   Light brown, diagonal   Sandstone and conglomerate

IGNEOUS ROCKS

    Qr   Bright green   Rhyolite and obsidian
    Tp   Red   Light colored intrusive igneous rocks
    Tr   Red and white   Rhyolite

Pleistocene Glaciation

Glacial Map of North America
Scale: 1 inch = 72 miles

1. On the basis of the Principle of Superposition, what are the relative ages of the four main Pleistocene till sheets?

2. What was the direction of ice movement in the vicinity of Chicago, Illinois; Fort Wayne, Indiana; and Mankato, Minnesota?

3. What were the likely controlling factors which determined the present position of the Missouri and Ohio Rivers?

4. Explain the lack of glacial deposits in the southwest corner of Wisconsin.

5. Pleistocene lake deposits are illustrated on the map by a horizontal pattern. What is the origin of the Pleistocene lake basin approximately 50 miles south of Chicago?

Exercise 18

PLEISTOCENE

Pleistocene Lakes	Blue horizontal	
Wisconsin Glaciation	Dark pink	Moraine
	Light pink	Inter-moraine
Illinoian Glaciation	Dark green	Moraine
	Light green	Inter-moraine
Kansan Glaciation	Light yellow	Glacial deposits
Nebraskan Glaciation	Yellow, vertical	Glacial deposits

Lunar Geology

Geologic Map of Mare Humorum
Scale: 1 inch = 16 miles

1. What geologic features can be seen on this map?

2. Using the Principles of Cross-cutting Relations and Superposition construct a sequence of events and geologic legend for the map area.

3. What are the evidences of igneous activity on the map?

4. What is the likely origin of the numerous craters in this area?

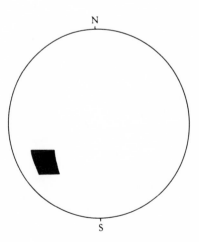

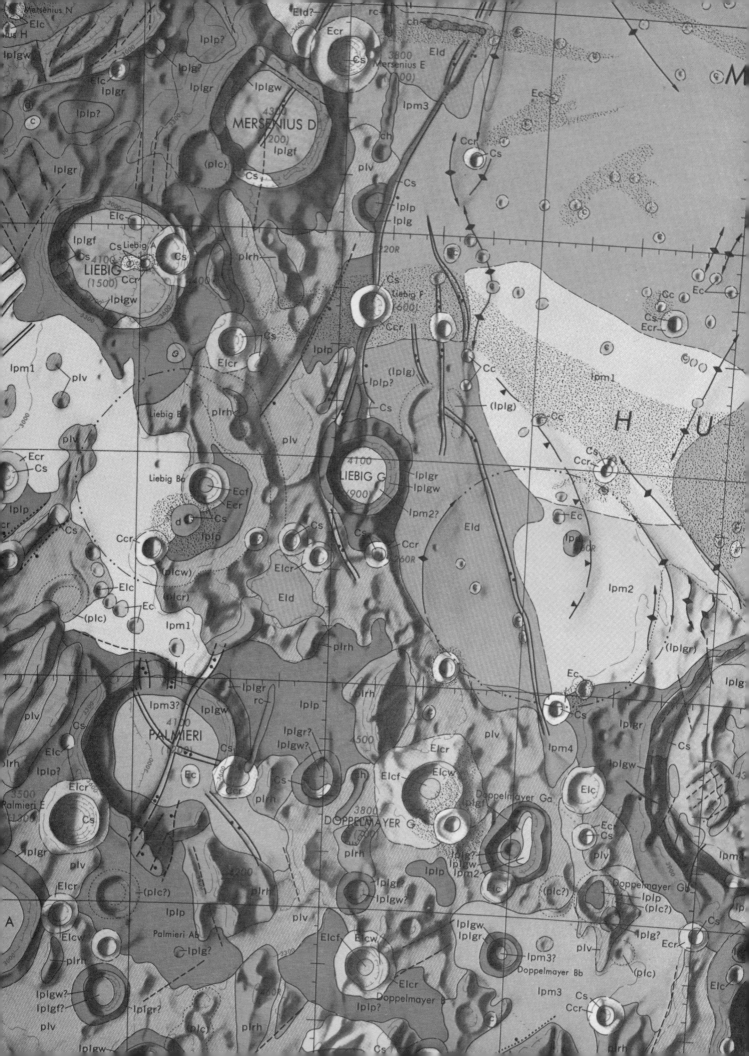

Figure 19-1. Full-moon photograph naming some principal features and showing the landing sites of Apollo 11 and 12. Official U.S. Naval Observatory Photograph.

115